Root into Europe

Myself to the forefront on the celebrated Champs Elysées. The monument behind my head –
the Arc de Triomphe at a guess – commemorates a Napoleonic victory of sorts.
Coincidentally, it is illegal in France to call your pig Napoleon.

ROOT

INTO EUROPE

Henry Root's journal of a fact-finding mission

The *Root into Europe* television series is produced by Aspect Film
and Television Production Ltd for Central Independent Television plc

BCA

LONDON · NEW YORK · SYDNEY · TORONTO

To Penny

This edition published 1992 by
BCA by arrangement with
Methuen London Ltd

CN 5498

All the photographs which appear in this book
are copyright © 1991 by Central Independent Television plc
with the exception of those on the following pages:
pp. 41, 72, 143 and 154 © Greg Evans International Photo Library
pp. 91, 93, 97 and 101 © Octopus Publishing Group Ltd
p. 152 © Philip Craven Worldwide Photo Library
pp. 33, 82 and 115 © Rex Features Ltd
pp. 104, 126 and 129 © Robert Harding Picture Library

Central logo copyright © 1989
by Central Independent Television plc
Aspect logo copyright © 1986
by Aspect Film and Television Production Ltd

*The Publishers would like to thank all those citizens of Europe
whose encounters with Henry Root are recorded in this book.
Special thanks to George Cole and Pat Heywood for making it possible
for us to reproduce pictures of Henry Root and Mrs Root.*

Photoset by Rowland Phototypesetting Ltd
Bury St Edmunds, Suffolk
Printed and bound in Great Britain
by Clays Ltd, St Ives plc

Contents

One   Esher   1

Two   La Belle France   13

Three   Gallant Little Belgium   39

Four   Hidden France   44

Five   Viva España   54

Six   Essential Spain   60

Seven   The Balearics   74

Eight   Arrivederci Roma   89

Nine   'Wilkommen, Bienvenu, Welcome!'   123

Ten   'Le Pays Bas: Nul Point!'   142

Eleven   Home Sweet Home   150

Mrs Root before departure. In her floral blouse from Bourne and Hollingsworth (Esher branch) she'll not be *à la mode* across the *Manche*, but I'll suffice for both of us.

CHAPTER ONE

Esher

Friday, 14th June 1991

I wake up strangely troubled, in the grip still of an unpleasant dream. I'm silent over breakfast, except to instruct Mrs Root to pass the chutney. I then confuse this with the plum preserve, spreading the latter on my toast.

'You've spread plum preserve on your toast instead of chutney,' says Mrs Root.

'I dare say I have, Mrs Root. The plain fact is I'm struggling with a large idea – though I don't know what. I had this dream, you see. About – excuse me – Mavis Nicholson.'

Mavis at One it had been, with Mavis chatting to Joanna Lumley about the latter's spiritual experiences on top of Everest. Suddenly, this reassuring midday image – two irreproachable women cross-legged on a settee in an English afternoon – had been replaced by one of Serge Gainsbourg, the little French crooner as was, and the news that, far from being dead, he was coming to London to meet Her Majesty.

I elucidate for Mrs Root.

'Grains of sand, isn't it? Final straws and so forth? *In re* 1992, I've remained calm, you'll agree, while the rumours multiplied: the demise of the British mile and Cox's Pippin, the news, reported in my *Telegraph*, that the SAS would be trained henceforth by Italian gymnasts. I'll not sit still, however, when *Mavis at One* is interrupted by a likeness of a Parisian *boulevardier* – the nose, the gauloise at an angle, the suggestion of *les liaisons dangereuses* in the early afternoon. We'll not want them in Esher.'

'It was only a dream, Henry.'

'Thin end of the wedge, Mrs Root. Had you done curry for supper I'd have hit the screen with a bolt of projectile vomit.'

I rise from the table, pace the room, pause for a moment beside the globe cocktail cabinet – an anniversary present from our neighbours, Sir Robert and Lady Mark. I offer Mrs Root a sherry wine.

'Not while I'm cleaning, thank you, Henry.'

I lift the Northern hemisphere, pour myself a drink – and then it hits me. I'll see for myself! A grand tour! 'The Root Report on Europe'!

'It's Europe for us, Mrs Root!'

'That will be nice, Henry.'

'Never mind nice, Mrs Root. This is work. A serious undertaking. Cometh the hour, cometh the man!'

'The Hoover's let me down again.'

'You're constantly confounded by the hardware, Mrs Root. You've prompted me to an analogy, however. The faceless men in Brussels can take care of the legislation – the nuts and bolts, the hardware, so to speak. I can't do everything. Only so many hours in a day, fingers on one hand and so forth. My concern will be the software.'

'The software, Henry?'

'Precisely, Mrs Root. Creeping characteristics, indigenous mores, Continental habits floating like bacteria on the wind. Only two ways of doing things – the English and the other. We'll not want the other here. Know your enemy.'

Mrs Root seems startled, asks who the enemy might be. I have to explain everything.

'The Continental, Mrs. Root. What's he up to? He'll be here, I tell you. Coming through the privet hedge on an English afternoon with a *baguette* akimbo and onions round his neck. He'll stuff *paella* through the letter-box. Post-1992 it will be Greek dancing in the High Street and goats in Tesco's. I read recently that more Greeks keep goats in their lounge-rooms than cats or dogs. We'll cross the Channel and catch them at it. Off guard. At ease with their trousers down. We'll paddle around in their laundry baskets.'

'In their laundry baskets, Henry?'

'I speak in metaphors, Mrs Root. I'll need official backing of course – a chit, as it were, from No. 10.'

Without more ado, I go to my desk, straighten my shoulders and pummel the keys of my upright portable.

In creative mood in my Esher lounge-room. Between myself and the bay window, signed likenesses of celebrities – Water Rats of one sort or another, Dickie Davis, Bonnie Langford, Paul Daniels, the little conjuror, Sir James 'God's Copper' Anderton – snapped at charity do's and chicken dinners. Beyond the window, my green suburban acre marches with that of my neighbours – Michael Aspel and his common wife.

The Prime Minister
10 Downing Street
London SW1

The Anchorage
Lakeside Avenue
Esher
Surrey

14th June 1991

Dear Prime Minister,

In the matter of 1992, you'll not mind my saying that the average man is not fully in the picture. Not your fault. From the summit, or presidential blow-out, you can't spot everything.

You've held our corner *in re* the fizzy lager and the onset of the two-pronged plug. But what Continental habits may slip through the tradesmen's entrance while you stand shotgun on the porch? Goats and garlic, isn't it, and a faulty attitude to what's proper in the afternoon.

So – I'm off to Europe to investigate mores you'll not be familiar with. I'll be introducing myself as your Man without Portfolio and would ask you to ease my path by dropping a word here and there through official channels.

Expect my report shortly.

Your Man at Street Level,

Henry Root

That done, I return to the cocktail cabinet and take a closer look at Europe.

'There's a lot of it, Mrs Root. It will take a month or more.'

'It sounds expensive, Henry.'

The woman has a point. We'll need funding. Commercial spin-offs, that's the dodge. A TV five-parter with my head in frame.

'Who's the little one, Mrs Root? The one with the legs and the comic hat?'

'Bernard Levin, Henry?'

'That's the one. Well done. *In Hannibal's Footsteps* was it? The printed voice-over to a six-week stomp through France – his liver as bloated as his musings by the end, I'd guess. He'll not mind my saying that he was let down by his wardrobe. Khaki army shorts worn below the knee are not suitable, in conjunction with a comic hat, for enlarged thoughts on camera *in re la condition humaine* and *soufflé au saumon*. I'll not make that mistake. A letter!'

Duke Hussey   The Anchorage
The BBC   Lakeside Avenue
Television Centre   Esher
Wood Lane   Surrey
London W12
                                           14th June 1991

Your Grace,

I've been deputised by the PM to look into Europe, spotting things he may have missed. It strikes me there's a major TV offshoot here – a parcel of films fronted by myself in which I'll elucidate changes post-1992.

Why me? I'll tell you. I'm not an expert, but that's in my favour, is it not? We British have a healthy disrespect for experts. Plus, I've not lately been abroad, not since being overcharged in Cardiff in 1958. I'll travel therefore with an open mind – though I've come to my conclusions.

Mrs Root will act as interpreter. She worked briefly at the Coq Sportif in Wigmore Street, once danced in a formation team in Belgium.

Expect research footage shortly. Account to follow.

Your man in frame,

Henry Root

Impressed at last by the weight of my intentions, Mrs Root suspends her dusting for a while.

'I say! When's this then, Henry? When do we leave?'

'Strike while the iron's hot, Mrs Root. The day after tomorrow.'

Mrs Root spins in circles like a top. She's ever thus when hit by a large idea.

'The day after tomorrow, Henry? I'll have things to stop. The milk, the papers – plus there's the cleaning to pick up. . . .'

They've minds like bollards, women. Just as you get up speed, the wind at your back, shoulders bunched over the wheel, you drive head first into a pile of wet cement.

'Stop things, woman? We haven't started yet! On the eve of an epic adventure you want to pick the cleaning up? No time for that, we're on our way. We'll start with France. Get that over with. I'll be there, oh yes, the PM's Cultural Attaché – on the Champs, up the boulevards, *al fresco* at the *brasseries*. "*Dos cafés con leche, por favor.* Chop chop, Gaston." That's where we'll catch them at it.'

'At what, Henry?'

'Talking, Mrs Root. The free exchange of ideas in the open air. We'll not want that coming across the *Manche*.'

'But we talk, Henry.'

'The Englishman talks, Mrs Root – "What's yours, Rodney?", "Funny sort of day, neither one thing nor the other", "I see the Arsenal were stuffed again" – but he doesn't *talk*. He isn't disputatious. Your Frenchman has an unnatural respect for ideas. We'll not want that in Esher. Ideas off the leash. Abstractions in the afternoon. Sartre, was it? And the other one.'

'What other one, Henry?'

'Never mind the other one, Mrs Root. I'll look into this. I'll merge. I'll quiz and probe and record my findings.'

I'd made my position clear, you'd think, yet Mrs Root was still disposed to grasp the stick by the wrong end.

'This is exciting, Henry. Paris is ever so beautiful, they say. We can see the sights!'

I hit that on the head.

'Notre Dame? Sacré Bleu? Is that your game? No time for that, Mrs Root. Into a memento shop perhaps. The four-by-six will render them well enough. Right! That's enough of that. There's work to be done. Organisation. Logistics.'

'Should I take notes, Henry?'

'No need for that, Mrs Root.' I tap my forehead. 'Mind like a lobster pot. Gathers info and retains it. Trick I learnt in the Navy. Where was I?'

'Organisation, Henry. Logistics and so forth.'

'Well done! So – there's shopping to be done. You'll be all right. You shopped last year if my files are anything to go by. A pair of oven gloves, was it? I'll visit Peter Jones. Leisurewear for the mature man. Socks by Lacoste, a lightweight blazer. I don't want to make the same mistake as the little one with legs.'

'Bernard Levin?'

'That's the one. I'll take as my model Percy Alliss the little golfer. He looks *àpropos* whether on the links or yarning in the snug bar with his pals. . . .'

'What about transport, Henry?'

'Precisely, Mrs Root. We'll go by road. Maps will be needed. That will be your department. Navigation and supplies. Backup and maintenance. Traditionally a woman's role. We're adequately stocked with Germolene, I take it? We have Elastoplast?'

'In the bathroom cabinet, Henry.'

'Well done. Plus you'll be on camera.'

'On camera, Henry?'

'This is a recce, Mrs Root. You'll film while I quiz. An *aide-mémoire* for Hussey. He'll want rushes as we go. Technical term. You'll catch on.'

'I certainly hope so, Henry. What about stills?'

'Still what, Mrs Root?'

'Photographs, Henry. Location shots.'

'Redundant, Mrs Root. A thousand words are worth more than a photograph, I always say. I shall encapsulate experience in prose, keep a daily journal, record discussions with little foreigners while the details are still hot in my head. Boswell, was it? Pepys? The peculiar one? Dined with the Cunard woman after hours?'

'Chips Channon, Henry?'

'That's her. Well done. A further thought occurs. I'm buzzing now. There'll be residuals. Franchises. T-shirts. Spin-offs. The book of the series! I must alert a publisher. Cape? The little American at Penguin?'

'Not Lord Weidenfeld this time, then?'

'I'd thank you not to mention Lord Weidenfeld, Mrs Root.'

The plain fact was we'd fallen out – a consequence of his not having asked me to his annual Christmas do in Cheyne Walk. I pitched up anyway, was headed off by a factotum in the vestibule. I breezed past him, entered the lounge-room, mingled with the usual crowd. Poseurs. Plagiarists. Fat men in dancing pumps. Old tarts in ethnic dresses with books on Wagner's love life up their sleeves. I engaged Princess Michael of Kent in a gentlemen's excuse-me. As we waltzed past, I heard the conceited one, the one who writes as if he's combing his hair in a looking-glass – Wheatcroft, is it? – observe that we reminded him of Abbott and Costello. Wheatcroft went head first into the punch, of course, but I was asked to leave. Still – bygones and so forth. Lord Weidenfeld didn't land up in Cheyne Walk by saying no to a certain chart-topper. I'd put this one his way.

My publisher, Lord Weidenfeld of Nicolson, muses on my offer of a pop-up book. Here's a chance, he thinks. 'Hold the presses!' he cries. 'There's one in the pipeline from Henry Root! Tell the Kent woman she can deliver late – if at all.'

Lord Weidenfeld of Nicolson
91 Clapham High Street
London SW4

The Anchorage
Lakeside Avenue
Esher
Surrey

14th June 1991

Dear Weidenfeld,

This one will be up your street. What we call a TV tie-in.
Financed by the BBC, I depart shortly for the Continent.
There's a pop-up book for the coffee-table here – a plain man's
guide to pints and plugs, plus, more importantly, pictures of
myself with goats and peasants.

'What's it all about, Pedro? Since we must die, why do we live
first? Speak up – you're on camera.'

I don't have to spell it out. You'll have seen Levin in the
Dordogne – draining vineyards, stuffing himself insensible and
sleeping it off in the patron's hammock ('*J'ai mangé miracles!*').
There's money in this kind of stuff.

Duke Hussey of the BBC is in.

Will forward contracts shortly.

Yours for a pop-up book,

Henry Root

That done, a further thought occurs. There'd be opportunities *en route*
for moneymaking speculations. How many goatherds, after all, can
you speak to in a day *in re la condition humaine*? On the Continent, not
least Rome, there'd be historic sites going for a song. With the right
partner and a wrecking-ball I could in a jiffy turn such locales into
high-rise hotels for overnight Japs. Store them in tubes, six feet long.
Japs don't need space, slot them into the wall on trays, as in a morgue,
ten to the unit.

'Space is money, Mrs Root. Who's the silly-looking one? Grins all the time. Bags of go. Around the world in a balloon. Across the Atlantic in a bucket?'

'Richard Branson, Henry?'

'That's the one. A letter!'

Richard Branson
The Virgin Group
120 Campden Hill Road
London W8

The Anchorage
Lakeside Avenue
Esher
Surrey

14th June 1991

Dear Branson,

We've not done business hitherto, but I have recently concluded that in spite of the PR stunts you're not as silly as you look.

Here's the dodge. I'm off to Europe shortly to recce a five-parter for our TV screens. Duke Hussey of the BBC is in, as is my friend Lord Weidenfeld of Nicolson.

I plan to keep an eye open *en route* for business opportunities that could do us both a bit of good. There'll be sites in Rome, I take it, suitable for a Little Chef or record shop. The Pantheon, is it? Equip it with a roof and you could hold a benefit there for the fat one who wears a frock. Boy George at a guess.

For credit purposes I'll drop your name. I trust you're liquid.

Henry Root

I'll treat with all sorts, not just those with a literary list. Richard Branson, the little *arriviste*, peruses mine of the 14th *ult*. With his money I'll acquire crumbling sites *en route* – the Appian Way, the Via Veneto – and franchise them back to Virgin plc as novelty shops and convenience cafeterias for fat Swedes and their yomping room-mates.

I doze in the afternoon, dream that *Ask Anneka* is interrupted by the news that Prince Edward has eloped with Madame Cicciolina, the little Italian MP who, to drum up business on the hustings, consistently poses in the buff as to her upper half and worse. I'm off to Europe in the nick of time.

Saturday, 15th June 1991

D-Day Minus One! I have my work cut out, but – with Mrs Root in tow – I carry all before me. First it's to Dixons in Oxford Street to purchase the photographic hardware. I explain to the little Asian who assists that the model must be of a professional standard.

'It has the zoom lens, does it? The cross-fade, the sudden rotation, the little dancers upside down? Money no object, you understand. Hussey will pay. Important mission, do you see? Into Europe for the BBC. Catching the Continental at it.'

My eye is caught by the display of flickering television sets to left and right. I knuckle the little Asian in the chest.

The changing face of Britain. Funded by my friend Duke Hussey and the BBC, I purchase hardware for the journey – video equipment to a professional standard. While Mrs Root masters the smart technology – the pan, the sudden zoom – I banter with the little Oriental salesman.

'Quality television – that's a concept unknown to your Continental. Post-1992, of course, he'll get the benefit of ours. *That's Life*, *Hearts of Gold*, *Carry On up the Doctor* starring Nigel Havers, *Brucie's Big Night Out*, Paul Daniels, the little conjurer. They'll not have had him before. Plus such as *Jewel in the Crown*. Several hundredweight of British Equity in boot polish above the neck. Excuse me, Sunil, no offence. How long have you been here, then?'

No harm in observing the courtesies, I always say, making these chaps feel at home. Which is something else we'll have to teach the Continental – English manners.

'Actually, I was born here,' he says.

We depart with camera, for the AA building in the Haymarket. I put Mrs Root in charge of maps, while I address myself to the matter of cross-Channel bookings and so forth. A lady with a hairdo taps the relevant information into a computer, asks me when we're coming back.

'I've no idea, madam,' I say. 'We're doing the whole of Europe. Could take a month or more.'

'I see. And what about accommodation?'

'Play it by ear,' I say. 'We'll not know where we are. We'll book on arrival. Mention my friend Sir Forte. As for insurance, I'll have the five-star Relay and the kidnap cover. A premium on my good lady. Italy's on the agenda, do you see? I'll want reimbursement if she's snatched. Where is the woman, by the way?'

I find her eventually at Accessories – dimmers, car rugs, warning triangles and so forth – where she has palled up with Mrs Perkins. Take your eye off a woman for a minute and she'll have found another with whom to discuss cling wrap, underfelt and biological detergents.

'This is Mrs Perkins,' says Mrs Root.

'Never mind Mrs Perkins,' I say. 'There's work to be done.'

'Mrs Perkins is going to Greece,' says Mrs Root.

'She'd be well advised not to do that,' I say. 'The men are addicted to the Greek vice and their great reeking women wear underclothes made from tea bags. You'll thank me for warning you, Mrs Perkins. Come! There's work to be done.'

We leave Mrs Perkins to cancel her holiday and head out into Leicester Square. Passing the Swiss Centre, I'm hit by a conundrum, slow down as I puzzle it out.

'Here's a conundrum, Mrs Root. Post-1992, there'll be Swiss culture, for what it's worth – yodelling in the pine trees, *après-piste* – but nothing extant still *in re* the Dutch, the Germans, the French and our good selves etc. We'll be subsumed, you see, under European culture. And what will that be, I ask myself. A blancmange. More accurately a cocktail – a bit of this, a bit of that. It will be Italians in clogs doing the German sausage dance round maypoles. Dame Lynn sings Edith Piaf. Spaniards in kilts, flamenco bars in Glasgow.'

'We'll have to hurry, Henry, or we'll be late for Tesco's.'

'Never mind Tesco's, Mrs Root. I'm struggling with a large idea. There'll be money in this, an opportunity for Branson. A Festival of European Culture! Funded by him, with myself as impresario. A large field or hippodrome, pay as you enter, an English tent, a French tent, a German tent and so forth. We'll collect turns as we go – the *jongleurs*, the bouncing Basques, fat Germans dancing under apple trees.

Remind me to alert the French Minister of Culture. Come Mrs Root! We'll be late for Tesco's.'

At Tesco's I load Mrs Root's trolley with drinking water, point her towards the breakfast products, explain that the Continental breakfast is a meagre thing.

'Half a *croissant* and hope for the best. Where's the bulk in that? To the roughage, Mrs Root! All-Bran, that should do the trick. And bread, do you think? They'll not have the sliced variety there. And some Eno's, I think, from the medicine display. In case the roughage is confounded by the *haute cuisine*.'

The prospect of all the disgusting meals ahead causes a sudden build-up of wind in the lower colon, and we have to leave – not before we're adequately stocked, however, with bread, water, roughage, toilet paper, tea and effervescent powder.

In Tesco's before departure, with a trolley-load of toilet accoutrements, English breakfast products and drinking water from a Wiltshire spring – Evian at a guess. Your Continental water has tadpoles swimming in it. Adequate for a Frenchman's weekly tubbing, but blending ill with the Typhoo One-Cup Instant. Your travelling Englishman would also be well advised to avoid France's automated public lavatories which now line the boulevards. An improvement on the sunken buckets which hitherto sufficed, they have already claimed eleven lives, including that of a member of the team sent in to investigate.

In the early p.m., while I'm composing letters in my head to the French Minister of Culture and, in the matter of law and order, to the head of the French Old Bill, a curious incident occurs. It's not my way as a rule to touch on intimate matters appertaining to the boudoir, but it's a telling episode, if I'm not mistaken.

Mrs Root, who should be packing, suddenly appears in the lounge-room wearing a red polka-dot dress.

'Goats and monkeys, Mrs Root! What's that?'

'Don't you remember this, Henry?' says Mrs Root, who has assumed a dreamy, somewhat halfwitted expression, not previously encountered. 'I wore it on our honeymoon.'

What was the woman talking about?

'Honeymoon, Mrs Root? Didn't have one of those, I'm glad to say. Too busy punching upwards. I didn't build up a chain of wet fish outlets by having honeymoons.'

'We had a night in Bournemouth, Henry. I wore this dress and we danced till dawn. You said I was the loveliest thing you'd ever seen.'

'I don't remember that, Mrs Root.'

I return to my letter-writing, reflecting that if I don't watch out she'll be packing the Carmen curlers and a cocktail frock, having in mind a night out at the Moulin Rouge or worse.

It's sad what happens to women.

The French Minister of Culture
The Ministry of Culture
Paris
France

The Anchorage
Lakeside Avenue
Esher
Surrey

15th June 1991

M le Minister,

Adios! You'll not know me. Undertaking a tour of Europe on the PM's wishes, I'll do France first. Get that over with. My brief is Continental habits, not least yours – but I have specific aims.

Here's one. A Festival of European Culture *in re* 1992. What do you say to that? Each country will mount its best in a Euro-field and info as to yours – snails and the Little Sparrow, is it? the *bidet* and the stomach-pump, the fat mayor playing *boules*? – will be most welcome.

I'll pitch up at the Ministry on arrival, rendezvous with you for tea and *croissants* and a comparison of cultures.

Branson's in.

Bonjour for now.

Henry Root

The Chief of Police
Paris
France

The Anchorage
Lakeside Avenue
Esher
Surrey

15th June 1991

Mon Brave,

While in France next week, I wish to compare law and order –
if you have it – with our notion of it here. There's more than
one way to put down a riot, they say. Plus, I wish to look into
the Continental criminal, who might be on us shortly.

I have advised the PM on policing in the past, and am
acquainted with Sir Mark, as was, and with Sir James 'God's
Copper' Anderton – an enthusiast for the hose and rubber
bullet.

I'll drop in on arrival.

Henry Root
Special Constable. Wet Fish.

CHAPTER TWO

La Belle France

Sunday, 16th June 1991

D-Day dawns. The epic adventure's on. We're up and running. Mrs
Root loads the Jaguar's roof-rack with four-square English products –
roughage, Eno's, Typhoo One-Cup Instant, Evian drinking water,
toilet rolls – while I supervise. It's a step into the unknown, but I feel
secure. My planning's been immaculate, we'll not be without provisions. There'll be English products in the European desert.

In no time we're out of the leafy Esher avenues and bowling down
the M25 to Dover. A stop for lunch at a Little Chef *en route* (our last
decent meal for a while, I fear) and we reach the harbour by half past
two. Here I keep on top of the situation at various checkpoints, am
able to tip the police off *in re* my suspicions as to the car behind.

'A word in your ear, Sergeant. In my view, the Volvo at my rear is
loaded to the roof with drugs. There's an SAS presence, I trust?'

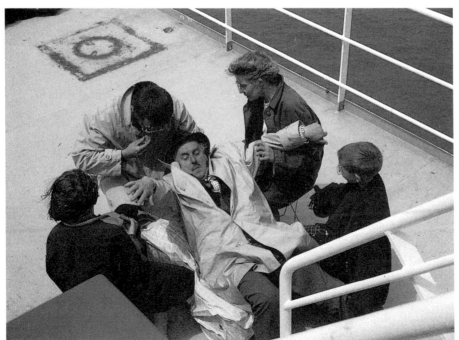

Ooh la la! Allez-oops! An audio-visual *aide-mémoire* aboard the ferry. During the dictation I inadvertently step into empty air and fall fifteen feet onto a party of picnicking French. The *Entente Cordiale* survives.

Up on deck I decide to mark the occasion with my first *aide-mémoire* for Hussey, instruct Mrs Root to get the camera out. She fiddles and focuses, eventually has my head in frame. I pace the top deck Whicker-like, modulate the voice to a professional standard. I'm working, after all, for the BBC.

'Audio-visual *aide-mémoire*. "The Root Report on Europe". Entry One. So – the mission's on. The die is cast. There's no turning back now. We're in no-man's-land. We're neither here nor there. Ahead the Continent beckons with all its attendant pitfalls – Sacha Distel, Gallic evolutions on the *duvet*, the *bidet* and the stomach-pump, livers as bloated as an actress's ego. Astern, the White Cliffs of Dover recede into the distance as per Dame Lynn. . . .'

I break off, render a few bars in an after-dinner baritone, step into empty air, fall fifteen feet onto a picnicking family. Damn silly place to put a stairwell, but, in spite of the duck *pâté* on my face, am able to lead the laughter. We British have a sense of humour.

'Dear oh dear,' says Mrs Root.

'Never mind oh dear oh dear,' I say. 'We'll visit the bridge, address the captain. Only polite to show an interest. It will be an unrewarding task driving one of these. Out of Dover, point it in the right direction more or less and two hours later you're tying up in Calais. What can go wrong? No wonder they drink too much. Follow me!'

We climb stairs, duck down corridors, find ourselves fifteen minutes later in the garage.

'We're in the garage,' says Mrs Root.

'I can see we're in the garage, Mrs Root,' I say. 'The layout of these ships leaves a lot to be desired.'

'Follow me,' says Mrs Root.

We find ourselves shortly at a door marked 'BRIDGE – NO ADMITTANCE TO UNAUTHORISED PERSONNEL'.

'Oh dear,' says Mrs Root. 'We'll have to go back.'

'Never mind go back,' I say. 'We're not personnel. Personnel refers to Frenchmen and civilians. A naval man such as myself is never personnel. A naval man is always welcome on a bridge. Come!'

I open a door, climb another flight of stairs. We're on the bridge.

'At ease! Don't mind me. Naval man myself. Keep your eye on the road, Captain.'

The Captain's impressed, glances briefly in my direction, then returns to his steering duties.

'Seems to be sober, Mrs Root. Oh yes – this brings back memories. The silent service. On the bridge in all weathers. Starboard ninety. Bombs away.'

I borrow the Captain's binoculars, scan the horizon for hostile shipping.

'"He clapped his glass to his sightless eye and I'm damned if I see it, he said." Newbolt, was it? They don't write them like that any more. Nelson. Drake. Lord Howard of Effingham. Lord Mountbatten of Burma, come to that. Hutch, was it, the big cabaret tenor? And the other one. Paul Robson, known, I don't know why, as Sanders of the River? We'll not go into that. Hullo – what's this?'

I've spotted the new technology, charting the course of other ships on a colourful radar screen.

Belay the mainmast, strike the mizen. I inspect the bridge, satisfy myself that the chap at the wheel knows the way to Calais.

'Angels one five! Sink the Frogs! I'd have had that one. Oh yes. There'd not have been survivors there. All's fair in love and war.'

The Captain's impressed, asks me what ship I saw service on.

'Ah. Didn't see service as such. Supply and demand myself. Pay and personnel. Laundry and so forth. An army marches on its stomach. I make the bullets and you fire them. Back-room boy. Essential supplies. I'll be off now. Come along, Mrs Root.'

'You've still got duck *pâté* on your hat, Henry,' she says.

'Well why didn't you tell me sooner, Mrs Root?'

Stupid woman. I could have made an exhibition of myself.

Once we've disembarked, the chief *douane* at Customs takes officious interest in the roughage on the roof. I give him a short burst.

'Henry Root. Wet Fish. The British PM's Man without Portfolio. On my way to meet your Minister of Culture. It'll be the axe for you, Pierre, if you confiscate the roughage. Doorman, if you're lucky, outside the Odeon in the Place Pigalle. Shame to waste the uniform.'

He backs off, allows me to proceed. I drive on, and then a thought occurs. I double back.

'A word in your ear, Pierre. The Volvo behind is stuffed to the roof with drugs. That's my view.'

A *douane* in a facetious hat (we'll not want hats like these when trooping the colour in the Mall – your British bobby on the beat always dresses sensibly as to his head) receives a burst for enquiring officiously about the English roughage on the roof-rack.

I feel better for the *contretemps*, reach the *autopiste* to Paris without further incident.

'Our first victory on foreign soil, Mrs Root. Stand up to the French and their heads go down. It's the same with their rugby players. Bags of flair and so forth, but knock them hard and they don't get up. It's plain sailing now. A man knows where he is on an *autopiste*. The services. The facilities. We could be anywhere. We could be approaching Birmingham. Straight through to Paris and an early night.'

'That will be nice, Henry. Where are we staying, then?'

'Only the best for us, Mrs Root. I'll aim at the Hilton, that's my plan.'

'Not very adventurous, Henry. Not very French, if you know what I mean. Shouldn't we try something more characteristic? This is a recce, after all.'

'In at the shallow end, Mrs Root. We'll not want an excess of culture shock. There'll be time for all that later. On our first night we'll want facilities to an international standard.'

'Perhaps we should have booked. It is the tourist season.'

'We're not tourists, Mrs Root! Great heavens! I'll mention my friend Sir Forte. There'll be a suite for us. We'll sleep like tops. Up early. Down the boulevard. Merge and mingle. Quiz and probe. In from an angle. Fly on the wall. I am a camera, Mrs Root.'

'I thought I was on camera, Henry.'

'A literary allusion, Mrs Root. Herr Issyvoo and Paula Bowles. We'll meet them in Germany, no doubt.'

'I'll look forward to that, Henry.'

'Don't be fooled by the Germans, Mrs Root. The men wear shorts and slap each other in the face with sausages. Anything left of the pork pie, by the way?'

Arrived at the Hilton, I instruct Mrs Root to oversee the unloading of the luggage and walk inside. I knuckle the desk, explain my business, ask for a suite with balcony, and fax facilities. To my amazement I'm rejected. There are no rooms available. I mention Sir Forte, Duke Hussey, the BBC – but to no avail.

I exit – with dignity, I think – recover tips sprayed around on entry, find Mrs Root struggling with the roughage.

'Never mind the roughage, Mrs Root. I've changed my mind. Didn't like the place at all. Not a good idea of yours. No soul. Piped music, a *piscine* on the roof with disco, Japanese businessmen at every turn. It might have been the Cunard Hotel, Hammersmith flyover. What we want is something typically Parisian. On the desk a monosyllabic crone in black, an aged porter, a creaky lift, an absence of plumbing, a bed like concrete. Follow me.'

'Won't that be something of a culture shock, Henry?'

'Never mind culture shock, Mrs Root. We're not tourists. This is a recce. How many times do I have to tell you?'

We drive around, find just such eventually, though God knows where. It could have been the Place Pigalle, equally the Champs Elysées. The crone has already taken to her bed, but an asthmatic porter leads us up some winding stairs, shows us a room of sorts, too small to swing a cat.

'This is agreeable, Mrs Root. Bags of character.'

I inspect the bathroom, suffer blow-back from the *bidet*, receive a dousing from the shower, return to the bedroom where Mrs Root, on all fours, seems to be in search of sockets.

'There doesn't seem to be a plug for my Carmen curlers, Henry.'

'You'll not need curlers, Mrs Root. You'll not be attending a *thé dansant* at the *palais*, joining a bingo club. We're here to work.'

'And there aren't any pillows, Henry. Just a bolster.'

'We'll place that down the middle of the bed. Separate sides. Trick I learnt in the Navy. Night ops. Two to the sleeping-bag. We'll not wish to become inadvertently entwined.'

'Nor we will, Henry,' says Mrs Root – in rather a wistful voice, I think.

There seems some danger she'll bring up stuff about honeymoons and so forth, so I put the lid on that. I bid her good night, balance a Ryman's Executive Memo Pad across my knees and write my journal up – recording, without boastfulness, I think, my first impressions of the Continent, how I've prevailed to date in every confrontation, corrected their thinking and sustained the English way of doing things. The proof's in the pudding, I think you'll agree, as you turn these pages in your English lounge-room.

That done, I climb into bed, entrench myself behind the bolster, turn out the light and shortly fall asleep – later dreaming, if I'm not mistaken, about the asthmatic porter appearing on *Ask Anneka* uninvited. We'll not want that. We'll not want French porters in proximity with Anneka.

Our first night on foreign soil, a French unaccustomed double bed. I enjoy the untroubled sleep of a traveller who has prevailed against the odds – the *bidet*, the *douche*, the stiletto-heeled *poule* in the street below, the barking *chien*, the bed like concrete.

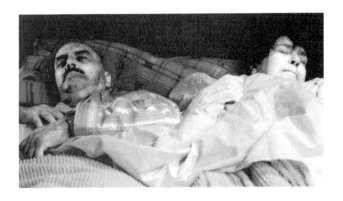

Monday, 17th June 1991

The first day of an epic undertaking. I'm up early, ready for the challenge. A bowl of roughage, then we descend to the vestibule, where Mrs Root's eye is caught by some tourist literature.

'An economy evening at the Moulin Rouge is it, Mrs Root, a charabanc trip to Sacré Bleu? No time for that. It's the inside track for us, the soft underbelly, the indigenous short cuts known only to the locals. We'll take to the boulevards as cultural fifth columnists, catch them with their trousers down. We'll *become* French. First I must find a *Daily Telegraph*, however.'

We're in luck. We go outside, discover that we're not two streets distant from the Champs Elysées. I find a kiosk, purchase a *Telegraph*, am cheered to find that the big lad Gooch has taken a hundred off the Calypso Cavaliers.

'Your little West Indians are like the French,' I explain to Mrs Root. 'Bags of natural talent, but hit them hard and their heads go down. Right – it's time to merge and mingle, take to the boulevards, get to grips with the place. Follow me, Mrs Root.'

We merge and mingle on the Champs. I could be a local, frankly – Mrs Root sticks out like a sore thumb, paddles along like a tourist, looking in the shops. I expostulate with the woman, instruct her in the Elysées stroll – the *baguette* at an angle, the head held high.

We reach the Champs. I lead, merge, copy the local walk – the easy nonchalance, the toes turned out – had I had a gauloise in my mouth you'd have taken me to be a Frenchman, God forbid.

'Blend, Mrs Root,' I say. 'You look like a tourist. Copy me. Trick I learnt in the Navy. Dropped behind enemy lines I could make myself invisible. One mistake – a bullet in the back. We'll take coffee now, *al fresco* at a café. Catch them talking in the open air. The start of our investigations. This one will do.'

We sit down, I summon up the *garçon*.

'*Dos cafés con leche, por favor* – and a piece of information, if you'd be so good. Where do the thinkers hang out?'

'*Pardon?*'

The fellow doesn't speak English. I enunciate more clearly, but retain a normal pitch. There's nothing worse in my view than Englishmen who think they'll be understood by shouting.

'The thinkers, Gaston. The enlarged head, the beard, the woolly waistcoat sprayed with tobacco ash. Sartre, was it? Plus his companion – Ninette De Beauvoir, if I'm not mistaken. As per our own Sir Worsthorne and the Lambton woman.'

'He's Dutch, Henry,' says Mrs Root.

'I dare say he is, Mrs Root. I was merely bringing it to the attention of Gaston here that we have philosophers too. Muggeridge, Levin, Booker, Wheatcroft, Paul Johnson, my friend and colleague, Wallace Arnold.'

'Sir Worsthorne and the Lambton woman,' says Mrs Root.

'He's Dutch,' I say. 'Try to keep up with the pace, Mrs Root.'

Either way, Gaston eventually catches on.

'*Ah! Les intellectuels!*' he cries. '*Les Deux Magots, peut-être.*'

'Them too, I wouldn't wonder. Make a note of that, Mrs Root. The two maggots. Where can we find them, then?'

'*Allez à la Palette*,' Gaston says – at which point an argument breaks out, as if to illustrate my point as to a Frenchman's disputatiousness.

Surely it was my friend Paul Johnson who incomparably observed that there's no such thing as an English intellectual. 'It is a purely Continental term,' he wrote. 'An English intellectual is discredited by his acceptance of the word.' *Al fresco* on the Champs, a single question triggers off a furious dispute.

To my left a businessman puts down his *Figaro* and starts to shout the odds. I scarcely follow him, but gather that in his opinion La Palette is far from being *à la mode*, further that the two maggots are no longer at the eye of intellectual fashion, an assertion that Gaston vigorously denies.

Then a chic lady to my right leans across and, unless my ears deceive me, says:

'*Sartre? Il n'était qu'un con!*'

You'll pardon my French. Then they all join in. Names are bandied hither and thither. A policeman stops and mentions Foucault. His absence from a podium with a whistle causes a traffic pile-up. A passing workman with a shovel compares Foucault unfavourably with

Derrida. Semiology is mentioned. The chef appears and laments the death of Barthes. Arms are waved, voices raised, shoulders shrugged.

'What did I tell you, Mrs Root? Ideas off the leash. Abstractions in the open air. We'll not want that in Esher. I gathered, however, from the tumult that our friends the two maggots are to be found talking the afternoon away on something called the *Banc Gauche*. We'll slip off now and catch them there.'

The discussion rages into the afternoon. Names of thinkers are bandied over the *croissants*, competing theories are cited and refuted. A helmeted street-cleaner suspends his scooping of – excuse me – *merde des chiens*. Time to depart for the *Banc Gauche*.

We leave the café in an uproar. I hail a taxi.

'*Le Banc Gauche*,' I say. '*Les Deux Magots*.'

'*Les Deux Magots?*' the taxi-driver says. '*Ce n'est pas à la mode. La Palette* . . .'

'Don't you start, Marcel,' I say.

We arrive shortly at the *Banc Gauche*, where I instruct Mrs Root to take the camera out.

'Am I in frame, Mrs Root? Well done. Right – here goes. Audio visual *aide-mémoire*. "The Root Report on Europe". Entry Two. It's

Paris now. *Le Banc Gauche*. Famously the haunt of thinkers. Sartre, Ninette de Beauvoir, the two maggots, the riots of sixty-eight, the baton, the hosepipe and the rubber bullet. Whack! Another student decked. I beg your pardon, madam.'

I break off to apologise. In my zeal I'd floored a woman with my *Daily Telegraph*.

'Forgive me, madam. I'm working for the BBC. Send your cleaning bill to Hussey. Where was I, Mrs Root?'

'The riots of sixty-eight?' says Mrs Root.

'Well done. Right – here goes. Audio-visual *aide-mémoire* continued. The riots of sixty-eight. The inevitable consequence of ideas in the afternoon. The brain rattling with caffeine and disruptive notions. The influence of German thinking to the left of centre. Marcuse was it? The Frankfurt School? The advocation of Expressionist dancing in the street? Naked students finger-painting one another after lunch? We know where that leads. Right! That's enough of that. To work, Mrs Root!'

I spot a café which is lousy with philosophers if I'm not mistaken.

On the celebrated *Banc Gauche*, I come across a covey of philosophers bandying abstractions in the open air. Small wonder the students rioted in sixty-eight, indulged in Expressionist dancing in the streets when they should have been at their books, or, better, on the playing-fields.

The corduroy jacket – sometimes velvet – the spotted handkerchief in red, knotted at the neck. A beard or two. I stroll between tables piled with bottles, enquire after the two maggots, have no luck. They've not been in, I think. I knuckle a thinker in the chest.

'Cheer up, Marcel! It may never happen! I tell you, Mrs Root, you could let off a bazooka here and not hit a normal type. Bohemians the lot of them. Drinking and talking and it must be half past three. We'll join that lot there. Blend, for goodness' sake.'

I sit down with twelve others at a table. I raise my hat.

'*Adieu* for now. Henry Root. Wet Fish. A writer like yourselves. You'll be familiar with my stuff, published for the most part by Lord Weidenfeld of Nicolson. *Henry Root's World Of Knowledge*. Common sense in a nutshell. A handy compendium of British thinkers. Muggeridge. Levin. Sir Worsthorne, the little Dutchman.'

'And the Lambton woman,' says Mrs Root.

'Never mind the Lambton woman, Mrs Root. So – philosophy, is it? A waste of time. What did Sartre tell us about the best way to skin a halibut? I'd not have built up a chain of wet fish outlets by reading Sartre – nor De Beauvoir, come to that. Practical intelligence, that's the thing. Intelligence in action. So – what's the problem? Allow me to assist.'

Marcel mentions something called Bernard Williams's Trap. Six archeologists ambushed up the Amazon by an Indian with a bow and arrow. The Indian offers them a choice. Either he kills all of them, or they choose one of their number to be sacrificed, thus allowing the others to escape. What should they do?

'Easy,' I say. 'Kill the fucking Indian. Excuse my French.'

'You miss the point,' Marcel says. 'We're discussing a moral dilemma here.'

'And a damn silly time to be doing it,' I say. 'In a swamp, up to your eyes in leeches, surrounded by Indians – and you want to discuss morality! Common sense, that's what's needed. Imagine this. You're six men stranded in hostile country. No food, no weapons and a little Jap is about to shoot you up the arse. Excuse me, Isiguro. Didn't spot you there at first. Been here long, have you? Where was I?'

'A little Jap is about to shoot you up the arse,' says Mrs Root.

I spin through 360 degrees, eyes scanning in a watchful arc.

'Do what! Goats and monkeys! Where?'

I twig what's happened, round on Mrs Root.

'What's your game, Mrs Root? Gave me a hell of a turn. Where was I? Never mind – I have it. The only way out is across a stream. You find a bucket and a length of rope.'

I instruct Marcel to stand up.

'Right. This is a bucket. That's the river. You're over here. Now, we need someone on the other side. Stand up, Pierre. So – how does Pierre pull you across?'

'But this is just a trivial riddle!' Marcel says.

'It's not a trivial riddle if Isiguro here is trying to shoot you up the arse,' I say.

I address another philosopher.

'Right, Philippe. You're in charge. What are you going to do?'

'Throw the bucket at the little Jap,' Philippe says. 'Excuse me, Isiguro.'

'You're catching on,' I say. 'A practical solution. Well done. Now – you lot over there. In England we make our own entertainment. We don't sit around after dinner and discuss the meaning of life. Games that test the intelligence, that's the thing. Right, Henri – you try and remove François's shirt without taking his jacket off. The rest of you, try balancing coffee spoons on the end of your nose. You never know when that won't come in handy.'

To divert their minds from disruptive notions, I set the so-called thinkers an exercise or two that test the wits, instruct them in *practical* intelligence, as per my friend Jeremy Beadle – how to balance a spoon on the end of the nose, the best way to remove a thinker's shirt without disturbing his jacket and so forth.

I've got them organised, I've seen enough. I tell Mrs Root we'll be moving on, once I've visited the john.

'They're like children, Mrs Root. Keep them amused, that's the thing. Idle hands etc. They'll not riot again. Excuse me a moment, I'll pay a visit before we go.'

I enter the café, locate the washroom, am about to do my business when I spot someone's had it away with the toilet bowl, leaving just a hole in the ground. On the way out, I encounter a woman coming in.

'You're right out of luck, madam,' I say. 'Someone's nicked the toilet.'

I join Mrs Root again, tip her off *in re* the burglarisation of the toilet.

'Goes to show you can't trust an intellectual, Mrs Root. Right – that's enough of that. Follow me.'

In the evening, while I try to get the shower to work, I inform Mrs Root that it's the *haute cuisine* for us tonight.

'That will be nice, Henry,' says Mrs Root, who's in the bedroom, reading a magazine.

'I don't know about nice, Mrs Root. It's the Tour d'Argent for us.'

'That sounds enjoyable, Henry.'

'Nothing to do with enjoyable, Mrs Root. This is work. My brief tonight is the Continental male, as exemplified by the Tour d'Argent's proprietor, one Claude Terrail. He's one of them, Mrs Root. A playboy. A seducer. A womaniser. Read about him in a magazine. Rang him up and mentioned the BBC. He rose like a

I've achieved my purpose, I leave the philosophers contented with their spoons. I'll wager the students wouldn't have rioted in sixty-eight had they been busy with their spoons.

mackerel to the sprat. He couldn't wait to get his head onto British screens. Frightful type. All nose and trousers. At the races with a woman half his age. *Après-piste* with Hungarian starlets. Took his business once to Hollywood. It was Gabor Gabor and others of that ilk. We don't want his type in Esher.'

'Nor we do, Henry,' says Mrs Root.

'Technique with the lights on, Mrs Root. What's best left to the imagination openly in broad daylight on the *duvet*. We all know we've got one. Acrobatics are for the circus ring, Mrs Root, not the bedroom. Such a type would be better advised to take a cold shower from time to time.'

I give the shower a final thump, receive a drenching. I towel myself down, return to the bedroom.

'The point is . . . Goats and monkeys, Mrs Root! What do you think you look like?'

While I've been battling with the plumbing, she's not been reading a magazine, she's had the Carmen curlers out, still worse, is now wearing the red polka-dot dress I'd expressly told her not to pack.

'Don't you remember, Henry? This is the dress I wore on our honeymoon. You said . . .'

'Never mind what I said, Mrs Root. No time to change now. We should be on our way. You'd better come like that.'

Later, in the bar at the Tour d'Argent, I take the opportunity – while waiting for this Terrail creature to pitch up for our rendezvous – to warn Mrs Root further as to the dangers inherent in being in proximity to such a type.

'The evening will be very appertaining to my research *in re* the Continental male and the likelihood of his bringing his habits through the Channel Tunnel. Our lads – the SAS – on the *qui vive* to collar drug fiends, can't spot everything.'

'I suppose they can't, Henry.'

'In fact, for the respectable Englishwoman, the Italian poses the greatest threat. He characteristically operates like a pickpocket, seduction and the act taking place simultaneously and without the lady concerned realising that anything untoward has happened. An Italian can have – excuse me, Mrs Root – relations with you in the bus queue and you'll not know about it till you get home that night. The French seducer, on the other hand, works in the open, takes his time, uses the eyes, modulates his voice unnaturally. He hypnotises his quarry. It's the rabbit and the snake, Mrs Root, the skunk and the mongoose. The respectable Englishwoman should avoid eye contact with a Frenchman.'

'I'll remember that, Henry.'

'Mind you, the Frenchwoman is scarcely any better. Stick thin, suspenders, sipping gin in a free apartment. He'll have one of them in tow, mark my words.'

Claude Terrail, celebrated *gastronome* and philosopher of the kitchen – so dubbed for his proprietorship of Le Tour d'Argent. A notorious *bon vivant* and womaniser. He'd better not try it on with Mrs Root. A *baguette* to the back of the neck and he'd go down like an ox in an abattoir.

Whereat, the man's upon us, albeit unattended. He's worse than his photograph. He looks like the one who was married to the other one. Yves Montand, is it? The nose, the sleepy eyes, the world-weary downturn to the mouth. He pats his hair, squeezes his eyes menacingly, emits a volley of Gallic charm.

'Claude Terrail at your service. *Enchanté, madame.*'

He bows over Mrs Root's hand, kisses it lightly.

'The skunk and the mongoose, Mrs Root,' I say. 'Be on your guard.'

I'm keen to eat, to get that over with, but Terrail suggests that he escorts us first round the Tour d'Argent's museum.

'Follow me,' says Terrail, 'I'll show you the actual table at which four emperors dined together during the siege of Paris in 1783.'

'This will be boring, Mrs Root,' I say. 'Try not to say anything foolish.'

'Here we are,' says Terrail proudly. 'This is the original cutlery which the emperors used and here's the menu showing what they ate. Food was in such short supply that animals were killed in the zoo and brought to our kitchens. As you can see, wolf is on the menu, and a rat stew.'

'Steer clear of the stew, Mrs Root, that's my advice,' I say.

Terrail then shows us photographs pinned to the wall of VIPs who, the wolf hotpot notwithstanding, have eaten without mishap on his premises. Kissinger, the little German; Richard Nixon and, I'm cheered to see, Sir Churchill and Her Majesty the Queen.

'Our luck's changed, Mrs Root,' I say. 'Her Majesty's not one for the Continental blow-out, preferring to wear her specs and toy with a slice of overdone mutton. There'll be something on the menu fit to eat.'

At this point, I'm glad to say, Terrail hands us over to the restaurant's captain, explaining that he'll join us later at our table.

Confronted by the restaurant's high opinion of itself – haughty French service, dishes revealed with a conjuror's flourish, lids boastfully removed to show *haute cusine* on fire – some would buckle. I take to it like a duck to water, ordering with confidence ('Thank you, Gaston, we'll skip the starters, I think, and plump for the dish of the day, plus two glasses of the house white, Frascati, if you have it, here's a franc for yourself') and engaging Mrs Root in conversation.

'Funny sort of day, Mrs Root. Neither one thing nor the other.'

'The carpet's ever so nice, Henry. I wonder how much it cost.'

Trust a woman to focus on the underfelt.

'I'm expecting the Arsenal to be stuffed again,' I say.

In the event, the pressed duck Tour D'Argent is acceptable and fortified by a double sherry wine, followed by a *crème de menthe*, I'm more than up to it when M Terrail joins us for coffee at our table.

Indeed, I'm able with a straight face to listen to him as he expounds his so-called philosophy of love, remain unabashed when he tells Mrs Root that he would like to join up every polka dot on her dress with his tongue (these chaps can't help themselves, no doubt), even take to him somewhat when he admits that the three men he has most admired have all been English.

Conversation piece. After the *haute cuisine*, Claude Terrail and I swap sophisticated *badinage*. 'Nice place you've got here, Claude. It must have set you back a pretty penny. Be on your guard, Mrs Root.' Visitors to Claude's place would be well advised to steer clear of the *canard pressé* unless they have the Eno's with them.

By the time he asks us if we'd like to see his private playroom, I feel we're almost pals, tell him on the way upstairs that I once had one of them.

'Well, we men need to get away from the little woman sometimes, right, Claude? Converted a cellar, installed billiards, darts and a lager bar. A den for when the boys came round. A place to yarn without the need to moderate the language. . . .'

Terrail's playroom, his inner sanctum, isn't as I'd have had it, but each to his own. The walls are covered with photographs of him beaming like a buttered crumpet between the rich and famous. Lana Turner, Prince Rainier of Morocco, Gabor Gabor – people of that ilk. I'd not sneer. My own walls testify to rendezvous with such as Sir Mark, Bonnie Langford, Dickie Davis, Lionel Blair, Michael and Mary Parkinson and Ernie Wise. If you know them – put them on the walls, that's what I always say.

Terrail asks me if I shoot. I think quickly, improvise.

'Shoot? I should say so, Claude! Well – shot, really, mostly in the past. Oh yes. Up early. Out on the moors. An aged ghillie biting into a pheasant turd to see which way the wind's blowing.'

I'm motoring now. I'll thank Mrs Root not to career in at an angle like a truck. I'm in luck. She's preoccupied, testing the accoutrements for dust, checking the underfelt. I continue.

'The looming stag. The castle battlements. The lone piper. The keening Scot sinking into his history. The leaping salmon – zap! I've got the bugger straight between the eyes, then I devil it over an open fire for breakfast. Those were the days.'

To my surprise, Terrail suddenly thrusts an elephant gun into my hands. He flicks a switch. A shutter at the end of the room opens to reveal a fairground shooting-gallery. He flicks another switch and a ping-pong ball rises on a stream of air in the centre of the target.

'A leaping salmon for you, Henri!' he cries.

Some would have bucked the challenge – I cock and take aim, score two bottles of vintage brandy, a glass lampshade and a signed likeness of Charles de Gaulle. Not my fault. The balance of the gun is wrong. I hand it back.

'Back to the gunsmith with this one, Claude,' I say. 'It's pulling to the right. Damn lucky I didn't kill someone.'

I decide it's time to leave. The research has gone well, I've come to my conclusions, though I can't remember what they are.

Later in bed – the bolster down the middle – I tell Mrs Root that my friend Claude Terrail isn't such a bad chap after all.

'You surprise me, Henry,' says Mrs Root. 'I thought he was quite disgusting. Mounting pictures of women on his walls indeed! Like stuffed trout in glass cabinets. He must be very insecure.'

You can't blame the woman, I suppose. A sheltered life and so forth. She'll not previously have met a sophisticated Frenchman.

'Live and let live, Mrs Root,' I say.

I visit the bathroom for an Eno's, get off to sleep eventually, dream, if I remember right, that as per a new initiative from Brussels *in re* Euro-monarchs, our beloved Queen Mum (God bless her) is to be phased out, her role on the Euro-stage being rendered in future by old Queen Juliana of the Netherlands as was; further, that in future Her Majesty the Queen will be required by community statute to take her holidays henceforth not at Balmoral – in gumboots and a headscarf, up to here in a freezing bairn or ghillie – but in the Balearics, whatever that might be.

I'm up at the sharp end in the nick of time, I think.

Tuesday, 18th June 1991

Prior to my main purpose of the day – researching the French idea of law and order – I put in a phone call from our room to the producer of the Jean Pierre Foucault show. It's my aim to guest thereon in the next few days.

Foucault is France's answer to Terry Wogan, more or less, with a peak-time audience of sixteen million mugs. He'll not pass up the chance of my chatting on his sofa.

The producer doesn't grasp my point at first, but once I've said who I am, described my connections with Duke Hussey and the BBC, with Lord Weidenfeld of Nicolson and so forth, he's keen to book me for the next day's show.

'Well done, my good man,' I say. 'You'll not regret it. I shape up well in frame, having previously appeared on *Ask Me Another* with Sir Day and so forth. I'm known in *Angleterre* as the man who says what others scarcely dare to think.'

At which point a thought occurs. Just as my friend Clive James always checks who the other guests will be before accepting an invite to a do or *salon*, so I prefer to know whose head will appear in frame with mine.

'A word before contracts are exchanged,' I say. 'Who will be the other guests?'

It's between Kirk Douglas and Anthony Quinn, the producer says.

'I have the ones you mean,' I say. 'The little American and the Greek. Either will be acceptable, though I'll not dance in the Greek mode. Zorba, was it? I'll not do that. I'll be in the green-room at seven for make-up and hospitality. *Bonjour* for now.'

I field Mrs Root, inform her that we're off now to look into law and order – if they have it. A hairy taxi-ride ensues, and seconds later we arrive outside the police station in the so-called Fifth Arrondissement.

I instruct Mrs Root to remain in the street, to set the scene, to do some travel footage – the pan, the wide shot, the sudden zoom featuring cornices and so forth – while I investigate inside. I leave her working, enter the station, knuckle the desk, explain my business to the duty sergeant.

'*Adíos.* I'm here to look into law and order if you have it. Research for the BBC. I wish, if possible, to catch chummy on the job. The beret, the striped jerkin, the jemmy at an angle. We'll not want him in Esher. The French Connection can stay on your side of the *Manche*, *merci beaucoup* very much.'

The sergeant appears to have no English, calls a superior on the phone.

'*Il y a un saucisson anglais ici, mon capitaine*,' he says.

'Now you're catching on, Maigret,' I say.

Captain Paulus, who now appears, is a different kettle of fish entirely – neat, alert, respectful. I introduce myself, hand him my card.

'Henry Root. Wet Fish. Special Constable. A friend of Sir Anderton – God's Copper. I was telling your sergeant here that I represent British television, am currently doing comparative research for them and the PM on law and order. While here, it's my intention to participate from the back of a patrol car, to be fully active in the sudden bust, the stop and search – "Spread yourself, Gaston, *por favor*" – I wish to see for myself.'

Captain Paulus is impressed, says it would be his privilege to take me on patrol that evening in his car, suggests I return at six p.m. to attend the night-shift briefing.

'*Merci beaucoup, Capitano*,' I say. 'You'll not regret your decision. Naval man, do you see? At my best under pressure. Eyes like a cat. Reactions like a cobra. I'll not let you down. *Bonjour* for now.'

I recover Mrs Root – kill time till the early p.m. (catch up with the *Telegraph* to be precise) and leave her in an agreeable little bar adjacent to the station, instructing her to wait for me there until I return.

'It's dangerous work this,' I explain. 'You'll be best off here, surrounded by respectable young people. I'll not be gone for more than an hour or two. Men's work this, you understand. The sudden arrest. The scuffle up an alley. "You're potted, Gaston!" Oh yes.'

Mrs Root seems momentarily concerned on my behalf. 'Are you sure you'll be all right, Henry?'

'Do not concern yourself, Mrs Root,' I say. 'I've a rolled-up copy of the *Telegraph* down my trousers. As good as a swordstick in the right hands.'

(*Left*) I deposit Mrs Root at an agreeable café – a haunt of students by the look of it – prior to my night on patrol with the French police. She needn't be concerned for my safety. With a rolled-up copy of the *Telegraph*, I'll match *les flics* in baton-wielding. (*Right*) From the captain's podium, I address the rank and file of the Fifth Arrondissement. What a shower! You'd not see British bobbies lolling and bantering at a briefing.

Mrs Root will be all right. Wife of a naval man and so forth. I leave her happily with her wool and knitting-needles, exit and cross the road for my rendezvous with my partner for the evening, Captain Paulus.

I attend the night-shift briefing and surprise the Captain, I think, by taking his place on the podium, addressing the troops with a few spontaneous words. I mention God's Copper – my pal Sir Anderton – refer to Churchill, Sir Mark, Lady Thatcher of Finchley, Lord Nelson, Trafalgar and Montgomery of Alamein. I use cricketing analogies, suggest we hit recalcitrants for six. Then I dismiss them.

'And be careful out there!' I say – an agreeable touch, unless I'm much mistaken.

Ensconced later with Captain Paulus in his car, I first quiz him about – excuse me – vice.

'The French attitude, is it? Turn a blind eye? On every corner, a lady of the night? Irma la Douce, is it? The fishnet stockings? The stiletto heels? The poodle in tow? Ignore them, do you?'

To my surprise, Paulus explains that there is very little street prostitution, except round the Bois de Boulogne, where, he says, most of the girls are in fact men – Algerian seamen, Brazilian transvestites hoping for the best.

'We'll not go there, thank you very much,' I say.

I change the subject, open up the matter of comparative police techniques.

'In England,' I say, 'things have improved greatly since my friend Sir Eldon Griffiths, MP introduced his Police and Criminal Evidence Bill in 1983. One of its provisions was that henceforth Old Bill's powers to stop and search included the right to carry out – you'll pardon my French, Captain Paulus – anal probes. As a result,

'*Bonsoir tous!*' The French community police introduce themselves informally to the local populace.

provincial police forces had, in the first six months of operation, recovered drugs with a street value of £180,000, seven vibrators, £23,000 in used banknotes, explosives, seven police truncheons, a gardening glove and a radio transmitter.'

Paulus surprises me by saying that such methods would never be allowed in France.

'You have trouble with the liberals, do you? Stirring it up? Making hearsay allegations? Calling "Foul!" if one of our Caribbean friends is questioned round the groin and kidneys? Inferring the whole barrel's rotten. My friend Sir Anderton . . .'

'God's Copper?' Paulus says. He's catching on.

'That's right. Well done! Sir Anderton once defined a good police force as one which employed fewer criminals than it caught. The French Old Bill? Stacks up in this respect, does it? Better that ten innocent men are banged up for a few years than that one guilty man goes free – that's what I always say.'

Paulus says that they receive very few complaints from members of the public – but he would say that, wouldn't he? I'm not stupid.

'Got a good PR machine working for you, I expect. Say no more. Man of the world. Nod's as good as a wink.'

I'm a little disappointed. The streets seem very quiet. I advise the Captain to liven things up by putting his siren on, but he demurs. I scan ahead in a watchful arc, on full alert for trouble. Eventually, I spot a student.

'There's one!' I cry. 'He'll be a dissident. Practise our baton technique, shall we? Whack! Another student decked.'

I leap from the car, floor the student from behind with my rolled-up *Telegraph*. I stop the traffic, usher an old lady up an alley – 'Pardon me, *madame*, there's a bust in progress' – attempt to cordon off the street. Paulus is impressed, but a trifle concerned, I think, that I'll steal his thunder. He asks me to get back into the car.

'Really, Mr Root! You'll have us all arrested!'

I have to laugh. 'Oh yes?' I say. 'Ha! Ha! Who by?'

Moments later, Paulus himself gets out of the car, talks to a blonde, mini-skirted young lady leaning on a lamppost, escorts her to the car and puts her into the back with me. She's a pretty lass. I'm about to say '*Bonjour*' when I remember in the nick of time Paulus's info *in re* Algerian seamen and Brazilian transvestites.

'Watch it, Gaston!' I say. 'Try it on with me and you'll feel the sharp end of my *Telegraph* up your arse. On second thoughts, perhaps not.'

Instead, I whack him crisply on the head – a warning shot, as it were – am a little surprised when Paulus says that this is his daughter Claudette.

'Sorry to hear that,' I say. 'A worry for you and Mme Paulus. How long has Claudette been at it, then?'

'At it?' says Paulus. 'I think I don't understand, perhaps. Claudette is in her last year at the Sorbonne. I sometimes pick her up here after an evening lecture.'

I've seen enough, instruct the Captain to drop me off at the café where Mrs Root is waiting for me, thank him for helping me with my research.

'You left Mrs Root at the Café Coq?' he says. '*Mon Dieu*! I hope she'll have been all right.'

What was the man talking about? I leave him and enter the Café Coq where, as I expected, Mrs Root has made herself at home. Two young ladies are reading her knitting patterns, while their friend, an obliging café guest, is cats-cradling Mrs Root's wool as she winds it into a ball.

While I've been on patrol, Mrs Root has palled up at the Café Coq with some local young folk – students, probably, from the local Sorbonne. 'One purl, two plain, cast off' – women's work. Fifi gets the hang of it, while the fellow with earrings watches carefully. An obliging tourist winds the wool for Mrs Root.

'Ah, there you are, Mrs Root,' I say. 'The low life in this city! You wouldn't believe it. Prostitutes, pimps, transvestites, pushers! It was touch-and-go a couple of times, I can tell you. Paulus was reassured to have me at his shoulder.'

'That's nice, Henry,' says Mrs Root. Then she introduces me to the two young ladies who are reading her knitting patterns. 'This is Jacques, and this is his friend, Pierre. They can't stay long. They have to be in the Bois de Boulogne by half past nine.' She nods towards the coloured gentleman who has been winding her wool, lowers her voice. 'Otherwise he gets cross with them.'

I'm in luck. I address our friend from the Caribbean.

'Evening, Winston,' I say. 'Don't happen to know the cricket score, do you?'

He replies with a volley of fluent French. I'm amazed.

'I say. Your French is very good. Been here long, have you?'

Wednesday, 19th June 1991

A red-letter day, my appearance on the Jean Pierre Foucault show. A word in the green-room with Quinn the little Greek, who's playing second fiddle ('Breathe deeply in the wings before your entry, Tony,' I advise. 'You'll be all right.') and then we're on. Afterwards I obtain a transcript of my performance, so that readers shouldn't miss a word or nuance of my gist. You'll agree, I think, that I gave as good as I got.

FOUCAULT: We are lucky indeed to have with us tonight Mr Henry Root, who describes himself as the British Prime Minister's Man without Portfolio, and his delightful wife Muriel.

Thunderous applause. Mr and Mrs Root enter down a staircase and are welcomed by M Foucault. They take their places on the sofa.

FOUCAULT: So, Mr Root. Could you describe the nature of your mission? You are the Prime Minister's Man without Portfolio?

ROOT: More accurately, I'm his Cultural Attaché, Jean Pierre, seconded to compare Continental habits with our own. It struck me, do you see, that post-1992 there'll be no such thing as French, Dutch or German culture *per se* as such. It will be European culture. A new mix, as I see it, a *mélange*, a hotpot, a stew – the meat and potatoes from Britain, of course, the condiments from other parts.

FOUCAULT: I see. You're suggesting that England will be Europe's cultural backbone?

ROOT: Naturally. With my associate Branson, I plan to mount a Festival of European Culture at a suitable locale, perhaps in France. I have in mind a large field with stalls and competing tents, a comparison of cultures. In our corner it will be the best of British, do you see? The Yorkshire Pudding Tent, that will be one. A display of Oxford

Marmalade, another. There'll be the British Sausage, the Queen Mum, God bless her, the Cox's Pippin. Plus a music tent – Dame Lynn rendering 'The White Cliffs of Dover'. You know it do you, Jean Pierre? Perhaps you'd like to suggest some French artistes? Edith Piaf – the Little Sparrow. She was one. *Je ne regrette rien.* Sacha Distel. *La Mer.* There'll be classical music. Hits from *La Bohème.* An 'Easy On The Ear' selection, £9.99. You could have a *pâté* tent, Jean Pierre, a garlic display – a cure for haemorrhoids, I've heard it said. Snails, *boules*, the lunchtime blow-out . . .

FOUCAULT: That's very interesting, Mr Root, but we'd prefer, I think, to be represented by Racine, Molière, the Comédie Française . . .

Vive la franchise! I top the bill on the Jean Pierre Foucault show. Jean Pierre, the studio audience and seventeen million mugs at home listen attentively as I inform them as to the new European TV schedules drawn up by my friend Sir Grade in London.

ROOT: If you say so, Jean Pierre. The choice is yours within reason, of course. What are they? Actors? And very adequate too, I dare say. However, in acting too we British lead the way, I think you'll agree. We'll mount excerpts from this and that, displaying the stiff upper-head school of English acting at its best – Sir Dance, the stuffed one from *Brideshead* – Irons, was it? – plus the fruity school, Sir Sinden – Dame Dench and the one who looks as if she's been in a fight. Dame Jackson? Plus there'll be a tribute to the English countryside. The fat lady sitting on a cow-pat. That means it's going to rain. Country practices, do you see? We'll not go further. Your countryside, Jean Pierre? Measure up, does it?

FOUCAULT: Of course. It is very beautiful. I assume you'll be visiting it as part of your research? If you want to understand French culture, Mr Root, you really ought to see the countryside.

ROOT: Rural France, is that it? The fat mayor? The braces? The bribery? The *boules*? Is that your gist? Well – if I must, I must. Put that on the list, Mrs Root.

MRS ROOT: What about pageantry, Henry?

ROOT: Precisely, Mrs Root. I was coming to that. I'll not need to tell you, Jean Pierre, that we British lead the world in pageantry. The royal 'do', the trees at attention in the Mall, the Queen attached by means of a surgical saddle to a horse.

FOUCAULT: One things strikes me, Mr Root. All the main attractions seem to be British. Is that your intention?

ROOT: Ah well, Jean Pierre – you must admit that the British way is best. Take your game, for instance. Television. We do it better, do you see? We involve the general public in sickness and in grief. Under the Euro-schedules you'll have a chance to see for yourself. You'll be able to tune in here to essentially English tragedies – an outrage in Oxford Street, an upturned launch – with the PM present at the victim's bedside, sometimes Fergie. Imagine that. You wake up in hospital after an outrage, come face to face with Fergie. Good TV. Plus you'll get Esther Rantzen. Abused tots and heart-swap rabbits interspersed with song and dance and garden carrots shaped – you'll pardon my French, Jean Pierre – like the male member.

FOUCAULT: And when can we expect this festival to open? Do you have the finance? Perhaps you should address yourself to Brussels. Arrange funding with the European Commission.

ROOT: Brussels, eh? Perhaps you're right. Put that on the list, Mrs Root. Belgium, is it? We'll go there first. Get that over with. Then we'll cover rural France. That won't take long. I'm grateful to you, Jean Pierre. It's been my pleasure talking to you.

Mr Root rises, shakes M Foucault's hand.

ROOT: Come along, Mrs Root. That's enough of that. *Bonjour* for now.

FOUCAULT: Thank you very much, Mr and Mrs Root! I'm sure we'll all look forward to your festival. We'll be back after the break, when I shall be talking to Anthony Quinn.

ROOT: The little Greek. I'll stay.

M Foucault ushers Mr and Mrs Root towards the staircase. They exit to thunderous applause.

Transcript ends.

Impressive, I think you'll agree. An historic testament to my current thinking, a document for the vaults and no mistake.

CHAPTER THREE

Gallant Little Belgium

Thursday, 20th June 1991

Up early, pack, a franc for the asthmatic porter – nothing for the crone in black – we load the Jaguar and hit the *autopiste* for Brussels, as per the advice of Jean Pierre Foucault. I like an *autopiste*. A man knows where he is on an *autopiste*, facilities every ten miles, convenience food in cafeterias which couldn't be better run by my friend Sir Forte. And in which, I may say, *Banc Gauche* intellectuals are unlikely to have had it away with the toilet bowl.

It's plain sailing, in fact, until we reach the Belgian border, where we are waved through without inspection. I stop the car, tap the *douane*'s window.

'Not so fast, Gaston,' I say. 'Why didn't you perform the stop and search? For all you know I could be a trans-European drug fiend. The packets of roughage on the roof-rack might contain a sufficiency of substances to decimate your country's youth.'

'Do they?' he says.

'No,' I say.

'On your way, in that case,' he says.

A disturbing exchange. Thank goodness for Lady Thatcher of Finchley who, before the cowardly stabbing in the back, saw to it that an SAS presence would stand at our Channel frontiers – whatever the latest, liberal Euro-regulations.

'A notoriously overweight and idle lot, the Belgians,' I explain to Mrs Root. 'Their customarily bloated expressions are caused by the fact that they carry food around in their cheeks to eat later in the day.'

All goes well thereafter until we reach Brussels where, due to inadequate navigational preparations by Mrs Root, we become temporarily misplaced.

'Not too encouraging so far, Mrs Root,' I say. 'We're more or less lost. We'll stop and ask. The language will be no problem here. Your indigenous Belgian is outnumbered four to one by your English-speaking Eurocrat.'

'Eurocrat, Henry?'

'Freeloaders, Mrs Root. Fat men on the gravy train, hands deep in the Euro-trough, wasps round a honey-pot. The subsidies and so forth. The backhanders. The lunchtime favours. The fix. The VAT. I refer to insider dealing. Nothing wrong with that, of course. We'll have some of that. A word with Sir Brittan and we'll be of their number. Ah – there's one. I'll ask him where we are.'

I stop the car, address a fat man with a bicycle.

'Pardon me, Gaston. Can you direct me to the Common Market?'

Gaston stares at me silently.

'Probably finishing his breakfast,' I explain to Mrs Root. I decide to repeat myself in French. '*Le* Common Market, *s'il vous plaît. Où est?*'

Gaston seems baffled, continues to stare at me in silence, seems suddenly to twig my meaning and replies in a language I'd not previously encountered. It sounds as if he's being sick.

'Just our luck to get a Norwegian, Mrs Root,' I say. 'Are they in as well, then?'

'I don't think so, Henry.'

'Thank goodness. The men are all inverts since the only available employment is on a whaling boat. And the women are little better, I'm told, seeking solace in Nordic myths and sordid introspection.'

'He'd have been a Walloon, Henry,' says Mrs Root.

'You're telling me, Mrs Root.'

'They're all Walloons, the Belgians.'

'Come come, Mrs Root. You surprise me. A bit sweeping that. Not fair to generalise. Live and let live.'

That said, I don't care to ask again, to seek assistance from a breakfasting Walloon, prefer to find the place unaided – am rewarded when, a mere hour or so later, we hit a building site with, at its rear, the so-called Berlaymont, a delightful building bedecked with European flags which, if I'm not mistaken, is the HQ of the Common Market.

I inspect a building site outside the Berlaymont. To entrepreneurs such as myself and Branson, there's a profit to be made from a hole in the ground. A subterranean shopping mall, perhaps, an underpass with boutiques and a Kall-Kwik Kaff, an automobile compound for touring Japs – the possibilities are endless.

The gravy train stops here. European Community Head-quarters, dubbed the Berlaymont. Following Euro-Regulation 768356b (the Non-Dissemination of Negative Information), it has not been revealed hitherto that because of fat EC functionaries falling out of upstairs windows after lunch the suicide rate in Brussels exceeds that of other European cities by a factor of 3.9865. It looks agreeable enough to me.

I park the car, negotiate the building site with Mrs Root. There's construction work to left and right. I like to see that. Wet cement. Holes in the road. A profit being made. We could be in Birmingham. My spirits lift. I'd not seen a bucket of wet cement in Paris. Nothing in the way of high-rise buildings going up.

I enter the Berlaymont, announce myself to an official behind a glass partition.

'Henry Root. Wet Fish. As seen on television last night. The Jean Pierre Foucault show. Myself and the little Greek. I'm here on behalf of Branson and myself *in re* Henry Root's European Festival of Culture.'

The official seems baffled. He scratches his head.

'You were right after all, Mrs Root. We've drawn another Walloon.'
I try again.

'Chop chop, Pierre,' I say. 'I'm here for funding. Kindly inform Sir Brittan that I'm in the vestibule.'

Pierre grasps my gist at last, puts a call in to a superior. Moments later an unnaturally tall young man appears, introduces himself – in Scottish – as Ben Gray, a *stagiaire*.

'A *stagiaire*, eh? And what might that be, young man?'

'A *stagiaire*,' he says, 'is a Foreign Office trainee, seconded for a term in Brussels.'

'Well done,' I say. 'I expect the Foreign Office knows what it's doing. I'm not here, however, to discuss my proposition with a short-term trainee. As I was saying to the Walloon here, I wish to see Sir Brittan *in re* funding for my Festival of European Culture.'

Young Gray explains that Sir Brittan isn't in Brussels at the moment, says that proposals of such importance are generally dealt with by a chap called William Martin – Head of the Unit for the Dissemination of Cultural Information, or something of the sort. Martin, it seems, is currently giving a lecture to a party of visiting businessmen, but young Gray is sure he'll see me later in his office. Meanwhile, it will be his privilege, he says, to show us round the building.

'This will be boring, Mrs Root,' I say. 'All right. Follow me, young Gray. Which way?'

There's little worse, in my opinion, than a conducted tour, so I enliven it by bringing Gray up to date with the latest Euro-regulations.

'Post-1992,' I say, 'Euro-TV schedules – drawn up in London by my friend Sir Grade – will require your member Continental to participate in three hours per week of Esther Rantzen and kidney-swap toddlers interspersed with amusingly shaped carrots contributed by viewers. And a good thing too.'

Young Gray's grateful to me for the info.

'Ah well,' he says. 'That will be culture, and the responsibility, therefore, of Department DG 4. I'm in Department DG 10. We have 18,000 people working here, split into twenty-two Departments, twenty-three if you include plugs and wiring, which is a bit of a hot potato at the moment.'

'The plugs will need changing, I hear,' says Mrs Root.

'Ah well, you'll have to speak to someone in DG 3 about that. Unless, of course, electrical current happens to be involved, in which case it comes under DG 17.'

'It all seems very efficient, dear,' says Mrs Root.

'A wee bit too efficient,' Gray says. 'As a matter of fact, this very building doesn't meet the stringent European Health and Safety regulations recently drawn up by DG 5. They'll be tearing the whole place down quite soon.'

This is enthralling, but I'm grateful nonetheless when we shortly come upon the lecture room where Martin, to my surprise, is addressing a party of businessmen in French – a circumstance I take up with him later in his office.

'Enjoyed your lecture, Bill. Don't know why it was in French, but you'll know your business best. What was it about, anyway?'

Martin explains that he was bringing a cross-section of French industrialists up to date with opportunities open to them after 1992.

'I'm a bit surprised to hear that, Bill. You, an Englishman, giving

(*Left*) I sit in on a seminar on Euro-sprockets for some visiting French industrialists. William Martin – a British citizen – gives them a leg up in their own language, I don't know why. He'll know his business best. (*Right*) In Martin's office, I describe my plans for a Festival of European Culture. I offer him participation on ground-floor terms (in Mrs Martin's name, if need be) but he seems reluctant to invest.

the French a leg up? You are English, are you? A bit off, surely. Industrial treason almost. Apprising the opposition of the dodges.'

Martin laughs – not condescendingly, I'm glad to say (had he been condescending he'd have got a burst at best, at worst a knuckle in the ribs) – explains that we're all Europeans now, that he works not for the British Government but for the Commission here in Brussels. After 1992, he says, we'll be European first – French, German or English second.

I'm silent for a moment, allow this large idea to shape up in my brain. My breathing becomes a little short, I'm undergoing a Damascus experience of some sort.

'European first and English second, eh? Is that your gist? We're all Europeans now, is that it?'

'Indeed,' says Martin. 'The future belongs to those who grab at new potential, those who are not confined to the wheelchair of old identities, old ways of doing things.'

I become more and more excited. I'll have some of the future, I'll not be left behind. If that's where the money is, I'm a New European. I'll have my hand in the Euro-honey-pot, I'll be aboard the gravy train. It's time, I judge, to get the finance for my Festival of European Culture. I describe it to Bill, explain that Branson and I are after further funding.

'Ties in nicely with your point, Bill, that there'll not be an Englishman as such post-1992, nor a Frenchman either, I'm glad to say. Equally, there'll be no such thing as English or French culture – what we'll have is a new concept, an original cocktail, the ingredients of which have yet to be defined. Will the English sausage prevail against the French *baguette*? Will it be Humperdink or Aznavour? The bouncing Basque or the keening Scot? The Queen Mum, God bless her, or old Queen Juliana? The Little Chef or the Tour d'Argent? So – are you in? I could arrange ground-floor participation for yourself on special terms. A numbered account in Switzerland – in Mrs Martin's name, perhaps. Might look better. Caligula's horse must be above suspicion. Say no more.'

Martin's impressed – I can see that – but he points out that a lot of ideas come in, that there's stiff competition for funding.

'And I can't just write out cheques willy-nilly,' he says. 'That's not my job.'

I've got one here. I'm losing patience.

'Whose job is it, then? I didn't drive two hundred miles for a meeting with the monkey. It's the organ-grinder I want to see. No offence, Bill. I'm sure you do your best according to your lights.'

That does the trick. I've straightened Martin up. He suggests that I send in written details of my scheme, at which point he'll see to it that the proposition is correctly channelled. He's keen that I stay, I can see that, but is equally keen that I get to work. He loads me up with helpful literature *in re* the latest regulations, plus relevant props and Euro-souvenirs – T-shirts bearing the message 'EUROPE – EUROPA', umbrellas, little blue and yellow Euro-flags and so forth, which he suggests I scatter as I travel. Euro-seeds to bear fruit later.

Mrs Root – piled high with promotional items – and I now leave Community Headquarters and step outside, where Mrs Root, unwilling, it seems, to negotiate the busy building site again, suggests that we take a taxi to the car.

'Nonsense, Mrs Root!' I cry. 'The stroll will do us good. Walk like a New European, for goodness' sake. The head held high. The shoulders back. The toes turned out. The future's ours. I tell you!'

CHAPTER FOUR

Hidden France

Friday, 21st June 1991

As we drive south in search of Hidden France, I feel a surge of confidence not hitherto experienced, not since we'd landed on foreign soil, at least. I have overcome all obstacles set in my path. I have a range of important new contacts. Jean Pierre Foucault. My pal Bill Martin. Captain Paulus of the Fifth Arrondissement. I have appeared to good effect on television. There is a feeling, even, that I have undergone some kind of spiritual experience in` Brussels. I liked Brussels. There was the sense of money being made, of restrictions and regulations being passed, binding on the common man. Restrictions and hygiene, that's what England has to offer Europe. That said, I've received the message. I'm a New European. I honk my horn at some overtaking Dutch.

'Tourists!' I shout.

'We're tourists, surely, Henry?' says Mrs Root.

'*Tourists*, woman? I should say not! We're in the forefront, at the sharp end, New Europeans on our way. We'll carry the message into Hidden France. They'll not have heard it yet.'

I scan ahead in a wide arc, spot a village clustered on a hill.

Hidden France, as per the Sunday supplements. It turns out not to be so well hidden after all. You can see it from the *autopiste*. I'd drive on, but for research purposes I'm obliged to stop. This won't take long.

'That will be it over there. Not so well hidden after all. You can see it from the *autopiste*. We'll head in that direction. This won't take long, I'm glad to say.'

I negotiate a *sortie*, head for the village, am nearly driven off the road by an old man with megaphone and stopwatch, waving his arms as we approach. Luckily I get him first, cause him to vault into a nearby ditch.

'Silly old fool,' I say to Mrs Root. 'He damn near got us.'

We drive on, approach the village down a narrow road, suddenly come face to face with thirty cyclists pedalling at top speed in our direction. Once more we have to thank my cobra-quick reactions. It's us or them, I drive straight through them, force them off the road, up side-streets, into the open doors of bars and cafés.

'We could have been killed, Mrs Root! Damn dangerous place, Hidden France. I'll fax Hussey with the info. He'll not have been here.'

I drive head first into some racing cyclists – a familiar hazard in Hidden France, of course. I keep my head, disperse them in all directions – up trees, into ditches, over garden walls. Pierre takes a header out of a café window. In France, unlike Italy, racing cyclists, for aerodynamic reasons, shave their legs. In Italy, on the other hand, all men shave their legs.

We find ourselves in the village square. A few shops, a bar, a small country market. Under a clump of trees, a group of old men are seaching for something in the dirt.

I elucidate for Mrs Root.

'Truffle hunting, Mrs Root.'

I park the car in the shade among the truffle hunters, instruct Mrs Root to arm herself with the Euro-literature, the guidelines, umbrellas, T-shirts and little flags.

'Bring the bumpkins up to date with our latest EC thinking, the word from Brussels.'

The sleepy village square. Is there *miel* still for tea? Stands the *église* clock . . . and so forth? The fat mayor takes time off from his civic duties to indulge with his pals in a tomato-throwing contest.

We head for the market, blend with the locals, move chameleon-like between the stalls – I do, at least, Mrs Root stands out, I fear. Melons are squeezed. Indignant chickens are held by the heels. Cheeses are sniffed. Mrs Root is overcome, wants to buy armfuls of regional *produit*, but I dissuade her.

'We're not here to enjoy ourselves, Mrs Root. There'll be plenty of time for the regional *produit* once we're back on the *autopiste*. I've not seen a service station yet which doesn't stock regional *produit* along with fax machines and toilet facilities for the disabled.'

'I expect you're right, Henry,' she says. 'But this is ever so charming, don't you think? Utterly unspoilt.'

'We know what that means, Mrs Root. Impossible to buy the *Daily Telegraph* and not a toilet an Englishman would use for miles around.'

'An Englishman, Henry? I thought we were New Europeans.'

'And so we are, Mrs Root. What I meant to say, of course, was not a toilet a New European would use for miles around. Come! We'll hand out some literature.'

I hand out bumf, distribute T-shirts and Euro-flags, advise a local *pâté*-monger that he should gear up for 1992 by investing in a freezer, inform a man with a goat that a plan is being hatched in Brussels to cut farmers' subsidies – the surplus going to Spanish tomato growers. The bumpkins are grateful to me, their humble rustic ways causing food for thought *in re* my Festival of European Culture.

'There are turns here, Mrs Root – the truffle hunters, the fat lady with the melon – who could be profitably displayed in a tent as part of my Festival of Culture. Foucault had a point, it seems. I'm glad we came.'

An animated rural
scene. Mrs Root
would be well
advised to steer clear
of the regional *produit*,
to wait for a Tesco's
to be installed with
adequate freezing
facilities and cling-
wrapped sprouts.
They'll not have
heard of *pasteurisation*
yet in France.

(*Left*) My pal Geoffrey. He's one of those – an Englishman trying to pass muster as a Frenchman. He'll get salmonella from the lettuce, be obliged to return to London to have his kidneys drained in Harley Street. Coincidentally, when the French doctors went on strike in 1987, the death rate fell by a surprising 7.03 per cent. (*Right*) I walk Geoffrey home past the fat mayor and his pals, now searching for their tomato in the dirt. To cheer Geoffrey up, I inform him that Branson and I intend to knock his house down and replace it with a BP diesel station. He's grateful for the early tip-off.

'But it's all so lovely, Henry. It would be a shame to break it up.'

The woman had a point. There could be money in leaving it as it was. Freeze it in time. Bottle their habits, as it were. There's a profit in conservation, as many a landed Earl has found. Bath. Bedford. The other one. The one with the boy who's always in the pokey. 'This is the commode used by George IV. Mind the lion, madam.'

'Keep it as a model village for punters from the *autopiste*? Is that your gist? A *tableau vivant* containing the fat mayor, the *boules*, the berets, the crafty peasants? You have a point, Mrs Root. I give you best. This village could be a permanent attraction, a living Pompeii. Stick in a couple of decent public toilets, a high-rise garage and a Happy Eater and we'd be away. The place is crying out for concrete. Ah – wet fish!'

I've spotted a fish stall, am momentarily diverted by an exchange between the man behind the slab and a thin, bookish-looking type – meagre English arms, comic legs, watery eyes – of the sort who comes to the Dordogne in August for the Continental blow-out and to catch up on his reading. Won't identify the village. 'Charming little spot – don't want the world and his wife pitching up,' he says in the pub back home. He'll be pleased to see me. I'll tell him about my plans with concrete. I tap him on the shoulder, raise my hat.

'Henry Root. Wet Fish. And this is the lady wife Muriel. Your first time in France, is it?'

The fellow seems quite displeased, I don't know why. 'No,' he says, 'I've had a house here for several years.'

He turns away, walks briskly off with his bag of fish – but I hurry after him.

'Really,' I say. 'In that case you'll be glad to know that its value will be rocketing in the near future. With my colleague Branson – or possibly Sir Forte – I'm planning a Festival of European Culture. This village will become a rural theme park, with a Happy Eater and toilets for the disabled. That house will have to come down. Not yours, I hope?'

He's bowled over by the news, his jaw drops, he can't speak, is working out the profit likely to accrue to him. I continue to fill him in.

'Come 1992, you see, there'll be no such thing as a Frenchman, John . . .'

'Geoffrey, actually. Geoffrey Burnstone.'

'If you say so, Geoffrey. No such thing as an Englishman trying to be a Frenchman, come to that. Don't mind me. Just my little joke. Bit annoying, I suppose. Thirty years trying to become something which doesn't exist any more! Back to square one. Oh well, that's life.'

I load him with Euro-literature and a range of promotional souvenirs – a T-shirt, a hat, a quiverful of little Euro-flags.

'You'd be advised to read the bumf,' I say. 'Acquaint yourself with likely improvements here post-1992.'

I leave him at this point and head with my handouts to the bar, last see him haring towards the local estate agent, where he plans to market his cottage pronto, I imagine. He'll be grateful to me for the early info.

In the bar I introduce myself to the locals, apprise them of the coming changes, hand round the literature, hats and T-shirts. I mention Branson and Sir Forte, describe our plans, mime a cement-mixer and fork-lift truck. They become very excited, smell money, assume crafty peasant expressions and show me photos of run-down barns they want to sell. I pocket these, say that we'll finalise arrangements when I return with Branson and Sir Forte.

Au revoir, Hidden France. These jovial rustics calculate the profit to be made when the old vicarage makes way for a tourists' outside toilet. They'll be able soon to remove their savings from under the bed and put them into the Alliance and Leicester (Dordogne branch).

'I'd like to stay chatting,' I say, 'but we're on our way to Spain. That church will have to come down.'

We bid them *bonjour*, return to the car and drive from the village – leaving behind an animated scene. The market stalls have been abandoned. Fat men in Euro-hats are measuring plots of land, identifying prime sites for me and Branson. The Mayor is pointing to the church, miming a wrecking-ball. Geoffrey emerges chalk-faced from the estate agent's little office.

'Gave them something to think about,' I say to Mrs Root. 'They seemed pleased enough and so they should be. They'll have amenities here undreamt of hitherto.'

We drive round a corner, come face to face again with the racing cyclists, who, after our last encounter, appear to have effected running repairs with bandages and so forth. I send them flying into ditches, over hedges, up side-streets and through the door of the same bar they entered hitherto.

'They damn near got me that time, Mrs Root.'

Back on the *autopiste*, Mrs Root seems inclined to whimper on about the local goods.

'I do wish I'd bought some regional *produit*,' she says. 'I really like that little village. It was ever so picturesque.'

'Never mind picturesque, Mrs Root,' I say. 'You'll learn more about the future of Europe on the *autopiste* than you will tramping across a field or watching fat men playing *boules*.'

'I'm not sure I agree with you, Henry,' she says.

I'm momentarily struck dumb. The last time Mrs Root disagreed with me was in July 1958, and I'd straightened her up on that occasion. I had since then taken power of attorney over her opinions – which a man must, of course, if he is averse to anarchy on the domestic front. Which is not to say that I'm unreasonable. Mrs Root rules in the kitchen, is queen of the cling wrap and Magimix – I'll not gainsay her in the kitchen.

'Do what, woman?' I say, having recovered the power of speech. 'The *autopiste*, as it happens, is New Europe in a nutshell, a metaphor, as you might say, for a better future. It's homogenised, do you see? We could be anywhere. None of your local colour here, I'm glad to say. In twenty years, the whole of Europe will look like this. You'll not know Somerset from Brussels. One giant *autopiste* facilitating commerce.'

I point to a road sign indicating that a service area with facilities is in the offing.

'And amenities like this for Eurocrats every ten kilometres. We'll stop here for the night.'

We pull into the service area, park the car and enter a delightful Novotel which, as I'd forecast for Mrs Root, features in its vestibule a display of local crafts and arts, little barrows piled high with regional *produit*, tended by a local lass in an ethnic dress.

'What did I tell you, Mrs Root? You can buy your regional *produit* here, Hussey will pay, but don't go mad.'

Before we register at the desk, I check the range of facilities on offer – a Euro-diner, an Executive Health Club with sauna attached, a *piscine*,

Back to civilisation. An *autopiste* complex with all the amenities for the travelling Euro-executive such as myself: a choice of hotels, competing *garagistes* and *boutiques* stuffed with shrink-wrapped vegetables.

a disco, a compound for those with children in tow.

'A New European could live here, I tell you, Mrs Root. You couldn't swing a cat here and not hit an amenity. Piped music in the lift, a Euro-bar, an Executive Grill-Room serving decent Euro-food, an adjacent *piscine* and a tumbler by the bed, I'd wager, for a Euro-Englishman to put his teeth in overnight.'

Mrs Root still seems doggedly disinclined to step into the future, to march to the new Euro-beat.

'But we could be in Birmingham, Henry,' she says.

'My point precisely, Mrs Root. You'll catch on.'

We dine in the Executive Rib-Room, repair to our technologically sophisticated Euro-suite for a well-earned early night.

'First time I've eaten in France without inflating like a rubber dinghy, Mrs Root.'

While I strive to master the Euro-control panel above the bed, Mrs Root turns over the pages of a pictorial tribute to the Dordogne, purchased against my wishes in the downstairs vestibule.

'I tell you, Mrs Root,' I say. 'A Euro-tycoon could run his business from here without leaving the Executive Lounge. Homogenisation, that's the thing.'

The woman seems disposed still to answer back.

'I suppose you'll be glad when Esher's homogenised,' she says.

'I was referring merely to your Continental Europe, Mrs Root. Your Gauls, your Latins, your little Greeks – they're the ones who'll need homogenising.'

'Well I think I preferred our hotel in Paris, Henry. At least it had character.'

'So does a barn in Dungeness,' I say, 'but you wouldn't want to live there. At the end of a hard day making money, a New European wants smart technology at his fingertips. Into bed, head down, sleep like a log.'

'With the lights on, Henry?'

'Just a question of mastering the control panel, Mrs Root.'

I punch some switches, cause the alarm to go off, bring the radio dramatically to life, turn on the bathroom lights. The lights continue to go on and off in sequence but resist my best efforts to douse them simultaneously. Eventually I strike the Euro-panel with a shoe. The TV comes on, but the lights at last go off. Suddenly the lights come on again, ignited, I think, by Mrs Root.

'What on earth are you doing, Mrs Root?' I say. She's not previously put on the lights without my say-so.

In our agreeable, technologically sophisticated bed-room, Mrs Root reads a picture-book, acquired from the hotel's well-stocked international vestibule. In due course I'll put a stop to this. Once our mission is completed, I'll not want the woman getting ideas in bed.

'Reading, Henry,' she says.

I'm lost for words. I wonder if this European venture is having an adverse affect on Mrs Root's character and morals. She's never read in bed before, I think, least of all when I'm intent on sleep. I'll have to watch her closely – I'll not wish her to pick up disorderly Continental mores. I'll not wish her to read books *in re* the Dordogne when we're back in Esher.

'Oh,' I say.

CHAPTER FIVE

Viva España

Saturday, 22nd June 1991

Up early, a help-yourself Euro-breakfast from a buffet, then back on the *autopiste*, heading for the Spanish border. In deference to the coming challenge, I slip 'Begin the Beguine', rendered by the little Spaniard Julio Iglesias, into the Jaguar's cassette facility.

'Not many people are aware, Mrs Root,' I say, 'that George Gershwin, the boogie-woogie songwriter, composed this with a black man sitting on his head. What do you make of that?'

'That's nice, Henry,' she says.

She's not been listening, she's got her head stuck into a guidebook on Spain, purchased the night before, I think, in the Novotel's vestibule. I'll have to put a stop to this. I shall be the source of info, she'll not need picture-books.

Once we're across the border, I start my informative commentary *in re* Spain.

'This won't take long, Mrs Root. Bulls and beaches. A primitive, riotous country pulled into the twentieth century by General Franco. Were it not for the General and the weather, the average Spaniard would still be living on a few pesetas a month and residing with his livestock and extended family in a stone hut under the ground. Thanks to your British holiday-maker, he can now seek employment as a waiter with a take-home pay of southern European standard.'

'They'll be grateful to us for that, Henry,' says Mrs Root.

'There is a dark side, however. I refer to Essential Spain. I've read about it in the *Sunday Times* colour supplement. The fighting bulls, the cruel landscapes, the whistling winds, the superstitious festivals involving donkeys. Death in the afternoon. We'll search it out, head for the interior. Not much fun, I don't suppose, but someone's got to do it.'

I have the woman's attention, she's abandoned her picture-book.

'I thought we were going to Barcelona, Henry. Is that esssential?'

'It is and it isn't, Mrs Root. Neither one thing nor the other. Crumbling old buildings round a polluted harbour – but with a smattering of high-rise flats for the lower-middle orders. A city of contrasts from all I hear.'

'They are hosting the next Olympics, Henry.'

'And a very odd choice too, if you ask me. Imagine it. Hotels half built. Little African athletes with their luggage in the street. The stadium a mud-flat at the off. An all-night disco next to where the British lads are lodged. The Olympic village built on a sewage farm.'

'That won't be very nice, Henry.'

'You're telling me, Mrs Root. The plain fact is the Spanish are unable to master simple drainage systems. At the marriage of King Juan Carlos, sixty-five portable turbo toilets were erected next to Madrid Cathedral. After the ceremony, the crowned heads of Europe and their consorts, including our own Royal Family, left by a side-door and walked into a septic tank. I see nothing but trouble ahead. The contract should never have gone to a third world country. Birmingham should have been the choice.'

We drive on down the *autopiste*, reach Barcelona's built-up outskirts. I'm surprised to find evidence of industrialisation – factories and so forth. Indications that the Spanish must, after all, manufacture this and that. I wouldn't trust a Spanish fridge myself, but there you are. Further on, we drive down wide avenues past glass-fronted sky-scrapers – the offices, it seems, of international corporations. I'm momentarily confounded.

'That's odd, Mrs Root. There must be commerce too. I wouldn't trust a Spaniard with my overnight money or funding stock. The Spanish businessman customarily wears yellow shoes. I'd baulk at a money-manager in yellow shoes.'

Further surprises are in store. In the city centre, smart shops and chic open-air cafés bulge with a sophisticated, cosmopolitan clientèle.

'We could be in Paris, Mrs Root. I'm temporarily nonplussed.'

'City of contrasts, Henry.' She consults her guidebook. 'It says here that we should visit the Avenue Ramblas.'

'My plan precisely, Mrs Root. We'll merge and mingle. Participate in the evening *paseo* with the stone-faced locals. I will, at least. The *paseo* is men's business, women do not by tradition participate therein. While their menfolk discuss matters of weight, the wives take coffee in small groups and chatter about underfelt.'

Mrs Root consults her guidebook. 'There's nothing about underfelt here, Henry,' she says.

'You've wasted your money in that case, Mrs Root,' I say.

We arrive at the Ramblas, a collection of narrow streets leading into a wide, tree-lined avenue busy with souvenir shops, open-air restaur-ants, kiosks and dark little bars selling squid and so forth – *tapas*, is it? I park the car, head for the central avenue, am immediately accosted by an ancient shoeshine man. I boot him from my path.

'On your bike, Pedro. Do I look like a tourist?'

We join the crowd on the Ramblas, blend with the throng.

'This is more like it, Mrs Root. You can smell Spain here. The anger, the poverty, the history, the drains. Stand fast, I'll join the *paseo*.'

I move against the flow, nod to the stone-faced locals.

'Afternoon, Pedro, a lovely day for it. Warm for the time of year.'

Having participated adequately in the *paseo*, I seek out Mrs Root, whom I discover in front of a cluster of cages dispensing birds, cats and rabbits. She seems displeased.

'This is ever so cruel,' she says. 'I've a mind to let them all loose, poor little things.'

The celebrated Las Ramblas. 'The most interesting street in the world.' Jan Morris, was it? 'You hear it first on the Ramblas,' they say – though what I'm not quite sure. The hoof-beat of history, perhaps. During our stay, I participated in the evening *paseo* but I didn't hear a thing.

'You'd not be thanked, Mrs Root. Cruelty towards animals is part of Spain's cultural inheritance. Take the bullfight. Pride and *machismo*. A fat man in ballet pumps with a frozen chicken down his tights. Death in the afternoon. *Olé*. A tragedy in three acts.'

'It is for the bull, Henry,' says Mrs Root.

'That's as may be, Mrs Root, but killing things and protecting his sister's honour are a Spaniard's chief concerns. Impugn a Spaniard's sister and he'll lock on to your leg like a fighting dog. We'll eat now. There's a Macdonald's over there.'

'But what about Essential Spain?' says Mrs Root. 'Shouldn't we merge and mingle? You are a camera, Henry.'

'You have a point, Mrs Root. I owe it to the mugs at home to sample the local fare. We'll risk it. Ah – here we are.'

I pause outside a café dispensing indigenous stuff *al fresco*, inspect its large photographic menu advertising *combinados*.

'This looks sensible – the *combinado*. Ham and eggs. Steak and chips. The mixed grill. We'll eat here.'

'Couldn't I have *paella*, Henry? I've always wanted to try *paella*.'

It's a good thing I'm with her. I tip her off.

'I'd steer clear of the *paella*, if I were you, Mrs Root. Rice and gubbins – the gubbins aspect seldom rewarding close inspection. Cat as a rule, often horse. Within hours of being tossed in the *corrida* a horse appears on the evening *à la carte*.'

Noblesse oblige. One of the more agreeable traditions retained from General Franco's day – the concept of proper Christian charity. Cheery beggars, and street tradesmen like this little shoeshine man, are obliged by law to rely on the goodness of others rather than on the state's largesse. If one doesn't require the service, one makes it clear. Lady Finchley would approve, I think.

Mrs Root's grateful for the info, as are a Swedish couple at the next table. They abandon their *paella*, settle the bill and leave.

'We're well placed for the bull run, Mrs Root. Front row seats.'

Mrs Root seems surprised. In spite of her tourists' picture-book she'd not been expecting this.

'The bull run, Henry?'

'Oh yes. There'll be one of them. In Essential Spain they always let a bull loose after the *paseo*.'

I summon up a *garçon*, order *dos combinados*, ask him what time the bull run starts. He doesn't seem to take my gist.

'*¿Qué?*'

'You know, Pedro. Several hundredweight of beef running up an alley. Fat men clinging to a lamppost. Old women hanging out of windows. Mad youths trampled underfoot. *Olé*.'

The *garçon* shrugs and wanders off. Mrs Root consults the glossary at the back of the picture-book.

'*A qué hora empieza* the bull run, Henry,' she says.

'Do what? Ah – I have you. Well done.' I address a party of young Spaniards sitting on our left. '*Adios! A qué hora empieza* the bull run, *por favor?*'

O tempora . . . and so on. I'm compelled to instruct this party of chattering young folk in their own cultural history. I make little headway. They can't even speak Spanish and their ideas seem to come from Italy. The lad on the right has a diamond in his ear, the little lass opposite wears yomping boots from Sweden. *Sangria* Socialists, they'd be more at home in Hampstead.

One of their number replies in a language I'd not previously encountered.

'Norwegians, Mrs Root. Just our luck.'

Another of their number then addresses me in English. He asks me what we're looking for exactly. I ask him where he comes from.

'Barcelona, of course,' he says. 'Are you on holiday?'

'Holiday! I should say not, young man. I'm a New European seconded to the BBC. I'm in search of Essential Spain.'

The young man seems mystified. 'Essential Spain? What's that?'

That's the trouble with the youth of today. It falls to a foreigner like myself to acquaint the locals with their history.

'Poverty, cruelty, superstition,' I explain. 'The slow march to slack drums at a religious turn-out. Men in hoods. Toddlers in make-up. The butcher's wife as the Virgin Mary.'

The party of young people still look mystified. I continue to explain.

'Leathery faced veterans who've never left the village. The gipsy tarantella. The ceremonial garrotting of a goat.'

The young Spaniard, the one who speaks English, seems quite shocked.

'That's terrible!' he cries. 'Is that what you think of Spain? Essential Spain today is design, fashion, new ideas. We've joined the late twentieth century, you know. You seem to be living in the past.'

I'm scandalised, but I keep my head. It's up to me to educate these callow younger elements.

'The past! I'm talking about your culture, Pedro. Would you betray your heritage? Where's your pride? Hemingway must be turning in his grave. When did you last face a fighting bull? Defend your sister's honour? Spear a tethered donkey at a distance?'

I break off, spot that, while I've been thus engaged, the little shoeshine man has been crouched under the table, covering my socks with brown bootpolish. I rise up in a fury, boot him backwards, fall over the table and lose my hat. One of the young Spaniards recovers it, dusts it down and hands it back – I'll say that much for him.

'Look, *señor*,' he says. 'If that's what you're looking for – the picture-book view of Spain – you might find it in parts of the interior, I suppose. But this is Catalonia. We are Catalans.'

I'm astonished. I turn to Mrs Root, whose fault this is.

'Catalonia! We're not even in the right country, Mrs Root. I blame you. You're in charge of maps.'

I address the Catalans, say that I'd be obliged if they could direct us to Spain.

'It's easy,' says one of them. 'Head south along the coast to Valencia, then turn left and keep driving. You can't miss it.'

We return to the parked Jaguar.

'Right,' I say. 'It's Essential Spain for us. What was it, again? Drive to Valencia and turn left? Onwards!'

'I don't know about that, Henry,' says Mrs Root, who is studying the map. 'If we turn left in Valencia we'll drive into the sea.'

'BASTARDS!' I cry. 'Pardon my French, Mrs Root, but that's the thanks I get for instructing them as to their history. Not that it was their history, I suppose – what with their not being Spaniards. We'll watch out for Catalans in future.'

Such incidents tend to harden one's resolve. I'd been growing soft – a fatal weakness when about one's investigative business. I'd lowered my guard, forgotten – because of my success so far – that you can't for a second take your eye off Johnny Continental. I drive south to Valencia, then inland, into the very bowels of Spain with a new hard-nosed determination.

CHAPTER SIX

Essential Spain

My spirits lift as the landscape becomes more desolate, I slip *The Man from La Mancha* into the cassette facility. I sing along. 'Dream the impossible dream. . . .' As we pass, leathery-faced old farmers straighten up and drop their oranges, donkeys stare in our direction, goats lose their footing and tumble into ditches. We speed deeper and deeper into the cruel interior.

I locate Essential Spain at last – the cruel winds, the grinding poverty, the unforgiving land-scape. It could be Wales. A primitive farmer with his mangy goat relaxes outside his crumbling *finca*. It wouldn't suffice for an English goatherd, but Pedro knows no better. Progress is a two-edged sword.

Dusk falls as we reach a tiny hamlet, no more than a cluster of primitive whitewashed cottages. It's not like me to blow my bags, but I can't help congratulating myself on having found Essential Spain so easily.

'There you are, Mrs Root. You couldn't get more essential than this. I told you I'd locate it. Naval man. Brain like a radar scan. Steer by the stars. You never lose it.'

I decide to look around, instruct Mrs Root to leave the car.

'Worth the long trek inland, I think you'll agree, Mrs Root. A century off the beaten track. They'll not have seen amenities here. It will be water from a well and the outside bucket. Right! That's enough of that. We've done Essential Spain. It's back to the *autopiste* for us. Come!'

I head back to the car, am surprised to discover that Mrs Root seems disposed to stay a while.

'But Henry,' she says, 'we've only just arrived. Surely we should get the flavour of the place. There might be something here for your Festival of Culture. And what about your mission to explain? The distribution of Euro-hats and so forth? They'll not have had Euro-hats and little umbrellas here.'

Our luck holds. We're centuries off the beaten track, but we find a *pension* that can put us up. At some inconvenience to the goat, no doubt, which will now have to bed down in the porch.

'You have a point, Mrs Root. Tell them to gear up. Accost a shepherd in a field. "*Adíos*, Pedro! You'll need a Filofax." Is that your gist?'

'Exactly, Henry. Couldn't we stay one night at least?'

'Stay, Mrs Root? Stay where? There'll not be a Novotel with Euro-lounge and *piscine* here, I'll wager.'

'There's bound to be something, Henry. A bed and breakfast place at least. We could knock on a door and ask.'

'Board and lodging, eh? Cheap but gloomy. A welcome in the hills. All right, we'll ask. Pass the phrase book. We'll knock a peasant up.'

I find the phrase for 'Do you have a room, Pedro?', knuckle the door of a primitive cottage.

'Watch out for the goats, Mrs Root. It's not the Hilton.'

'That's true, Henry,' she says. 'But nor was the Hilton.'

'We were fortunate to get in anywhere, Mrs Root.'

The door is eventually opened by an immeasurably old peasant woman dressed in black. I raise my hat.

'*Bon noche, señorita.* Henry and Muriel Root – fellow Europeans.' I hand her some Euro-literature and a flag. '*¿Tiene usted una habitación?*' I mime a man asleep.

The ancient peasant woman seems a little startled – the lateness of the hour, no doubt. At last she answers.

'*Sí. Claro.*'

'We're in luck, Mrs Root. First place we ask, they have a vacancy.'

'Perhaps we should look at it first, Henry.'

The woman has a point. Naval man, used to sleeping rough, but one would prefer not to bed down with the goats. I consult the phrase book again.

'*¿Podemos verla, señorita?*'

The old lady shrugs indifferently. She's not going out of her way to welcome us. Business must be brisk – a reassuring sign.

'*Sí.*'

We enter the house. I'm pleased to discover that the interior is spick and span. Simple – a table, four chairs, a cabinet – but clean. A little old man in a beret – the chef, I take it – pokes his head round the kitchen door. A pleasant smell of cooking wafts in our direction.

'Evening, Pedro,' I say. 'Our luck holds, Mrs Root. We seem to be in time for dinner.'

The old lady takes us upstairs, shows us our bedroom. I look inside the wardrobe, am surprised to discover that clothes are hanging in it.

'Probably keep some of their stuff in here when they don't have any guests,' I explain to Mrs Root.

'At least it's clean,' says Mrs Root. 'Basic but clean.'

I give the old lady the thumbs up. 'We'll take it,' I say. 'Right, Mrs Root. We'll get the luggage up. Doubt if they run to a porter here.'

We return downstairs, fetch the luggage from the car. In our absence, the front door has been closed and bolted. I hammer on it with some impatience. At last the old woman opens it, seems a little startled. We enter with our luggage, make for the stairs.

'Give us five minutes to wash our hands *señorita*,' I say, 'and we'll be down for the first sitting.'

We unpack, partake of a quick wash and return to the dining-room where, I now notice, the table is only laid for two.

'We're in luck, Mrs Root,' I say. 'We must be the only people staying here. The service will be good.'

We sit at the table, wait for our dinner to be served. After a while the old woman comes out of the kitchen and lays two more places at the table. We are then joined by the chef in the beret.

'Small establishment like this, Mrs Root,' I say, 'off the beaten track, not unusual, I imagine, for the chef to eat with the customers.'

The old lady places a large pot on the table, removes the lid. I peer inside, sniff suspiciously.

'What is it, Henry?' asks Mrs Root.

When supper is served in the simple dining-room, you'll note that the chef (*right*) joins us for rabbit in the pot – an agreeable local custom, I imagine. It would be unusual, I think, for Mosimann, the little Swiss, to have joined his punters at the Dorchester for the evening *à la carte*.

'Chicken in the pot, unless I'm much mistaken, Mrs Root.'

The old lady ladles out a portion each. Mrs Root takes a mouthful.

'I think it's rabbit, Henry.'

'Of course. Rabbit *au pot*. I should have known. Very Essential. There's only enough for two, I see. Just as well we're the only guests.'

Over dinner, I initiate a conversation. 'All set for 1992, are you? A little place like this, bags of local colour, rabbit *au pot* and so forth, you'll be knee-deep in Euro-salesmen. Plus there'll be Euro-entrepreneurs such as Branson and myself with development intentions. You'll have to gear up of course. Install a switchboard and a fax machine. Put a Euro-lass on the front-desk. . . .'

My conversational initiatives hit fog, I have to say. I start to yawn. It's been a long day. I suggest to Mrs Root that we have an early night. We bid the old couple *adíos*, retire to our room.

'I wonder where they sleep, Henry?' says Mrs Root. 'There only seems to be one room.'

'They'll bed down with the livestock, Mrs Root. A poncho, the flickering embers. Odd, really – a comfortable bedroom like this and yet they prefer to sleep with the goats. Just goes to show – you can lead a peasant to water, but you can't make him drink. It will all change after 1992, of course. I'll inform them in the morning.

The chef and his lady – waving Euro-flags – bid us *bonjour*.
Thanks to me, they'll be adequately geared up for 1992. By next year they'll have installed a fax machine and a Euro-lass in reception, plus a seminar room for conferring Euro-salesmen.

Sunday, 23rd June 1991

We sleep well, considering, wake to find the pension deserted. The chef and his lady will be at the market, I imagine, or snaring a rabbit for tonight's guests. I can't hang about – there's the rest of Spain to do – so I leave a bundle of pesetas on the kitchen dresser and depart.

We head south again, shortly landing up in a village which identifies itself as Mora De Rubielos. Slightly larger than the little hamlet where we spent the night, it seems to have one of everything, as in a Western: a square, a bar, a drapery store, a church – and, I wouldn't wonder, a priest, a judge, a doctor, an undertaker and a sheriff. It's a one-horse town. I decide to stop and look it over. We park the car, stroll into the deserted square.

'The young men will be out in the unforgiving countryside,' I explain to Mrs Root, 'tending their goats and tilling the barren soil. The old men will be yarning in the bar, the old women will be cleaning their simple homes and preparing bean stew for the evening meal. Come! We'll visit the bar.'

In Mora De Rubielos, a stone-faced local meditates on the mystery of things under a monument. Coincidentally, seventy-six per cent of the men in Essential Spain still clean their teeth by chewing on a stick. In Wales, the figure is eighty-three per cent.

In Essential Spain the village elders while the afternoon away in a local bar, while their women toil under the burning sun. Just as they do in Asia, as I explain to Mrs Root.

Gnarled veterans are playing cards. They glance impassively in our direction, continue with their game.

'Well, Mrs Root, what will it be?'

'I think I'll have a sherry wine, thank you, Henry.'

'You'll be lucky, Mrs Root. We're not in Esher now. I'll check with the barmaid. Do you stock sherry wine by any chance, my dear? Tio Pepe as a preference.'

'*Sí, sí. Claro.*'

'You're in luck, Mrs Root. They seem to have it. *Uno* sherry wine, my dear, *uno* gin and tonic and something for yourself.'

I direct Mrs Root's attention towards the old men playing cards.

'They'll have seen it all before, Mrs Root. The things they could tell us if only they could talk.'

'What could they tell us, Henry?'

'You've got me there, Mrs Root. Bugger all, probably. Let's not get stuck with them.'

The barmaid serves our drinks, and, noticing my interest in the buffers playing cards, identifies one of their number – a distinguished old gentleman with silver hair – as the local judge.

It would be only polite, I think, to introduce myself. I approach the table and raise my hat.

'*Adíos.* Henry Root. Wet Fish. My card. Investigating Essential Spain *in re* 1992. What's yours, Your Worship? A Tio Pepe, perhaps? They've just started importing it here, it seems.'

The Judge, who has no English, grasps my meaning nonetheless, is happy to accept my hospitality. I order his drink, give him some background on myself.

'Bottoms up, Your Honour. You'll be interested to hear that I myself applied to become a judge last year. Well – a magistrate, to be more precise. In Esher. Sent in the relevant papers, but haven't so far heard a thing. All in good time, I dare say. These things can't be processed overnight.'

For the Judge's benefit, I mime a magistrate sentencing a youth to a short sharp shock, suggest a wig and robes, hammer thin air with an imaginary gavel. The Judge grasps my gist, understands that I too am a judge, or the next best thing. Our relationship, in spite of the language problem, is cemented. It takes one to know one – even in Essential Spain – we're peas in a pod, His Honour and I.

'Oh yes,' I say. 'Respect for law and order? It's changed since our day. Only yesterday, the lady wife and I left the Jaguar unattended for an hour in Barcelona. We dined *al fresco* – a *combinado* each – and returned to the car to find a gang of street toughs about to steal the roughage. I dispersed them with my *Daily Telegraph*. I tell you, Your Honour. . .'

The Judge, who may not have grasped everything, reacts strongly to mention of Barcelona.

'Barcelona?' He almost spits the word.

'That's right, Your Honour. It's in Catalonia.'

His Honour takes a step back, puts a hand over his heart, I fear he may be about to suffer an attack. He recovers, lets off a volley of invective against the Catalans. I cannot altogether follow him, of course, but get his meaning more or less. When types like us come across each other a shared grammar of understanding transcends mere verbal skills. I distinguish certain words – 'Separatism', 'Anarchy', 'Irreligion' – nod in vigorous agreement.

'I'm with you all the way, Your Honour. Liberalism off the leash – drugs, peep-shows, *señoritas* going off like firecrackers on the Ramblas as if they were French or worse. They should be locked up, the lot of them.'

I mime a cell door being closed, a key being thrown away. The Judge nods enthusiastically, embarks on a short mime himself, which confounds me for the moment. I gather at last that he's inviting me to leave the bar, to accompany him across the square, where he wants to show me something of importance.

'My privilege, Your Honour,' I say. I turn to Mrs Root. 'This will be boring. I'm off to see his goat. You'll be all right. I'll return shortly.'

We depart together, negotiate the square.

'The thing is this, Your Honour. The concepts of freedom, democracy, liberalism and so forth are all jolly fine in theory, but they can be carried to excess in practice. As in so-called Catalonia.'

Mention of Catalonia gives rise to another short burst of disapproval from the Judge.

'Absolutely, Your Honour. In Barcelona, on the Ramblas, I fell in inadvertently with a party of young Cat— – I'll not say the word – bearing in mind your heart condition. Anyway, the men wore ear-rings, the women yomping boots from Sweden. They were on fire with the new freedoms, the new ideas – some from Italy, I wouldn't wonder. No sense of history, of their inherited culture. And what do these ideas amount to? Interior decoration, the most telling way to point a disco strobe. Nothing wrong with democracy, of course – for those mature enough to handle it – but the baby's gone out with the bath-water, that's my gist. Out goes repression and with it down the plug hole go decency and order. And what might these new freedoms be? Drugs and tubular furniture. The General must be turning in his grave.'

We have arrived, I now see, at the village court-house. I'm hon-oured. The Judge wishes to display himself in action. Fellow jurists and so forth. We enter the courtroom. It isn't the Old Bailey, but no doubt it serves its purpose. An ancient table, behind which the Judge presides. A dock for the guilty party. A cluster of legal books. Benches for an audience. The Spanish flag. A likeness of Juan Carlos on the wall.

'Very adequate, Your Honour. You'll have sent a few down here, I wouldn't wonder. Six years. *Olé*! Cruel but kind, stern but stupid. They'll thank you in the long run. You'll not mind if I have a go myself?'

I position myself in the Judge's place, gavel the tabletop, consign to the pokey those who consistently, in my opinion, fail to measure up. A practice run prior to my appointment as an Esher beak.

The law is the true embodiment of every-thing that's excellent. In turn the local judge and I gavel the tabletop, bang up dissidents and activ-ists. It's a toss-up as to which exceeds the other: his condem-nation of *La* so-called *Passionella* or mine of Lady Antonia Pinter.

'His Honour Judge Henry Root presiding! Lord Scarman – five years! The Pinter woman – ten years! Jeremy Paxman – fifteen years! Dawn and French. The Noisy One. The Big One. The Black One. The Other One – twenty years! Dame Warnock – life!'

The Judge applauds, wishes to have another turn himself. We gavel the tabletop alternately, bang up liberals, anarchists, moaning minnies, *Guardian* readers and the stage-army of rent-a-mob militant activists.

'Jonathan Dimbleby!' I cry.

'*Los Catalans!*' says the Judge.

'The Kinnock woman!'

'*El País!*'

'Arthur Scargill!'

'Francis Drake!'

'Belt up, you silly old goat!' I cry. I've heard enough, decide it's time to return to the bar, to gather up Mrs Root and head elsewhere.

I steer His Honour from the court-house and across the square. I dismiss him outside the bar.

'That's enough of that,' I say. 'I'll be off now. Moving on. I've done Essential Spain, unless I'm much mistaken.'

The Judge seems disappointed, mentions a *fiesta*, is of a mind to detain me, I think, until it's over. I demur.

'A *fiesta*, eh? The dour procession, is it? The superstitious march? Tots in make-up? The tethered goat? We'll miss that, thank you very much.' I pump the Judge's hand. 'The pleasure was mine, Your Honour. If you happen to be in Esher, look me up. *Bonjour* for now.'

I enter the bar, discover Mrs Root alone at the card table, counting her winnings. The barmaid is the only other person here.

'Hullo, where's everyone gone? You didn't offend them, did you, Mrs Root? Beat them at their own game? Always a mistake with your indigenous Spaniard – though easily done. Pride, do you see? They've not had much to celebrate since Lord Effingham sank them in 1588.'

We walk to the door and step outside. The *fiesta* seems to have begun. People are cheering. A band plays. Young men hang from buildings.

'This is agreeable, Mrs Root. Local colour. Mind the bull. Jumping Jesus! The bull's loose!'

The bull and I eye one another from a distance of three feet. I keep my head.

'Don't panic, Mrs Root. I've got this under control. Don't let it know you're afraid. That's the secret. Bulls can smell fear. Stand absolutely still.'

'What now, Henry?'

'Run like hell!'

Mrs Root and I take off like the clappers, make it to the barrier inches ahead of the bull, swallow-dive to safety and race to the car.

Discretion is the better part of valour. There's only one way to handle a bull in a shopping mall: leave the mall. Mrs Root and I vault the balustrade in the nick of time. Lucky for her that I was there.

'Damn me, that was a close-run thing,' I say. 'Lucky for us I kept my head. I'm getting the hang of Essential Spain, I think. We'll do more of it. Head south.'

'If you say so, Henry. Where to?'

'You tell me, Mrs Root. You're the one with the guidebook.'

'I was reading about flamenco, Henry. That sounds enjoyable.'

'A dance for tourists, Mrs Root. A fat lady on a table in a banjo bar. Shipped in from Neasden, as often as not. We'll miss the flamenco, thank you very much.'

Mrs Root consults her picture book. 'There's nothing here about a fat lady from Neasden, Henry. In fact it says that flamenco in its traditional form can still be seen in Granada, where gipsies perform it in their homes. That must be ever so interesting. I'm thinking about your Festival of European Culture. As yet you haven't booked a Spanish turn.'

The woman has a point. I'm not concentrating hard enough on my Festival of Culture. I should have booked the Judge. He'd look indigenous with his gavel on a podium. A counterweight to my friend, His Honour Pickles. I'll have Pickles in the English tent next to the Yorkshire Pudding.

'Do let's go to Granada,' continues Mrs Root. 'We can see the Alhambra at the same time. It says here that it's one of the seven wonders of the ancient world.'

'I draw the line at wonders of the ancient world, Mrs Root. There'll be more than enough of them in Italy. We'll skip the Alhambra, thank you very much. A tourist trap for our friends the Japs. However, the little gipsies dancing in their lounge-rooms sounds Essential. We'll head for Granada. Don't argue. My mind's made up.'

We drive south, back the way we came, through the cruel, unforgiving landscape. I slip 'Granada', rendered by my friend Sir Secombe, into the Jaguar's cassette facility. I sing along.

'Gran-aaada di-dum-dum di-dum-dum di-dum-dum . . .'

As we speed through the bleak, unaccommodating countryside, leathery-faced old farmers – the same ones as we encountered previously, no doubt – straighten up and drop their simple shovels, their donkeys stare in our direction, their mangy goats leap for safety, lose their footing, tumble into ditches.

We reach Granada late at night but park, undaunted, in the back streets of the old town, set out in search of the traditional flamenco. We wander round, get lost, are rescued at last by a barefoot street urchin tugging at my sleeve.

'*Flamenco, señor?*'

The urchin motions us to follow him, takes off at speed, dives down side-streets, up deserted alleys.

'Good idea of yours, Mrs Root,' I say. 'He's probably leading us into a cul-de-sac where the rest of his gang will mug us. Keep a grip on your handbag, that's my advice. I shall wield the *Daily Telegraph*. They'll not get the money-belt and traveller's cheques.'

To my surprise, we suddenly find ourselves in a gipsy enclave, a small square up a flight of steps, surrounded by whitewashed caves. A gipsy family, standing outside their cave, invite us into a long, windowless room lined with chairs. The family – father, mother, aunts, granny, teenage girls, small boys – are dressed for the flamenco. There are guitars and drums in evidence. We are offered wine, invited to sit down. I'm impressed, I must say.

'What did I tell you, Mrs Root? Straight into their lounge-room. We've found the real thing. A musical evening in the home. We're privileged to see it.'

We take a glass of wine, make ourselves comfortable on chairs. Mrs Root surveys the room.

They say of the Alhambra (*left*) that the more you look at it, the less you know. I discovered one thing, however. Eighty-six per cent of the souvenirs on sale in the adjacent gift *kioskos* (little tarantella dancers, table lighters shaped in the likeness of the Virgin Mary) have been manufactured in Wolverhampton and Taiwan.

'Do you think they're expecting others, Henry? There are a lot of chairs.'

'It's a large family,' I explain. 'Some will sit it out while Granny has a go. Don't concern yourself. We're off the beaten track, a distance from the tourist circuit. Few are as well informed as I.'

I click my fingers, beat a light tattoo with my holiday brogues, emit an encouraging volley of *olés*.

'All right, madam! Let's get the show on the road! We're privileged, I tell you, Mrs Root. Not many will have seen this before. Take it away, Grandpa! *Olé*!'

At this moment, and rather to my surprise, a party of little Japanese gentlemen and their ladies arrive at the door. Tickets are collected, a guide directs them to sit on chairs. Suddenly we have been surrounded by polite, chattering Japanese. I am momentarily confounded, but recover quickly.

'A special night, I dare say, Mrs Root. A cultural delegation from the East. An exchange is in the offing, I expect. We're fortunate to be here.'

The music strikes up, a sudden swirl of skirts, a rattle of maracas, a stamping of patent-leather shoes. I take this opportunity to explain the history of flamenco to the cultural delegation from the East – its finer points, the story behind the traditional songs.

Far from the madding crowd. On the outskirts of Granada, I track down the indigenous dance as done in a gipsy cave. I inform our fellow guests that flamenco dancers traditionally learn their skills by hopping about on burning coals.

'It's to do with suffering for the most part, Isiguro – as you can see from the expression on Pedro's face. Lost love, separation, yearning – that sort of stuff. *Blood Wedding*, was it? Revenge and so forth. A chap visits a lady of the night, discovers it's his sister. Oh dear. *Carmen Jones*, was it? Oscar Hammerstein II? Bulls are involved. Death in the afternoon. Pass the wine, there's a good chap. *Olé*!'

Isiguro thanks me for the info, passes it down the line, the family dances enthusiastically in turn. I clap my hands, stamp my feet, howl like a wolf in unison with Grandma.

Eventually I've had enough. I've exhausted myself, what with singing along plus doing a commentary for the little Japs. I clap my hands, pronounce the matter ended.

'That's enough of that! I'll be off now. Thank you, Pedro. A delightful evening. Come along, Mrs Root.'

We make for the door, where we're sand-bagged by a gipsy, who demands 50,000 pesetas for the evening's entertainment.

'Not such a good idea of yours, Mrs Root. You should have listened to me. It would have been cheaper to be mugged by the street urchin. Never mind. We'll send the bill to Hussey. We'll overnight here, depart early in the morning. I've done Essential Spain, I think. It's back to the twentieth century for us.'

'Oh yes, where are we going, Henry?'

'We'll make for the beaches, Mrs Root. A break for ourselves, plus we'll investigate the European by the sea.'

CHAPTER SEVEN

The Balearics

Monday, 24th June 1991

I decide, prior to departure for the beaches, to mark the fact that Essential Spain is in the bag (and to appease Mrs Root, who is complaining still that she's not allowed to see the sights) by shooting an *aide-mémoire* for Hussey on the steps of the Alhambra. We position ourselves accordingly after breakfast and I instruct Mrs Root to aim and focus.

'Right! Are you ready, Mrs Root? So – Audio-visual *aide-mémoire*. "The Root Report on Europe." Entry Four. The mission continues. I've covered Essential Spain. Bulls, poverty and superstition. Plus the little dancers in a cave. I've penetrated into parts not visited since 1836, I'll wager, and reacquainted insolent Catalans with their heritage. It's time to move on. To return to civilisation.

'The Balearics. Inhabited twenty years ago by two peasants and a goat, they became an instant leisure complex overnight – high-rise hotels squatting cheek by jowl round a dirty bay. In August, I've heard, an indigenous population of some 2,000 mushrooms to twenty million. The ideal spot to investigate the European by the sea, his annual general with the family. The Germans performing priapic pyramids. The French undressing without discretion, displaying – excuse me, Mrs Root – boastful pubic bushes, reeking of garlic. The Dutch drinking lager all day out of cans, thereafter wading knee-high into the sea where they urinate like horses. The Balearics then! Onwards!'

Driving from Granada towards Valencia, where I plan to catch the ferry to the Balearics, we pass a furniture factory adorned by Euro-flags. I'm struck by an idea.

'A little Spanish factory, Mrs Root. We should stop and investigate. Give them the benefit of our experiences in Brussels. Mark their cards. Acquaint them with the latest Euro-regulations. Plus, there could be an opportunity for Branson here.'

'But I thought we were doing beaches, Henry?'

'All in good time, Mrs Root. If the small, manufacturing Spaniard wishes to participate on the European business stage we'd better check he's up to it. We'll not want Spanish practices in British boardrooms. The *mañana* attitude. The sudden flare-ups *in re* their sisters. The yellow shoes. The lunchtime blow-outs. The long sleep-in in the afternoon. We'll not want stomach-pumps and yellow shoes in British boardrooms. Follow me.'

I park the car, enter the reception area with Mrs Root, announce myself to the *señorita* behind the desk.

'Henry Root. Wet Fish. My card. The Managing Director, *por favor*. Important business.'

A couple of phone calls from the *señorita*, and I'm in the Managing Director's office. I check his shoes, which I'm glad to see are black.

'He's over the first hurdle, Mrs Root. We might do business.'

I address myself to the Managing Director.

'I'll come straight to the point, Juan. I'm a busy man, as I dare say you are. Off to the Balearics tomorrow.'

'They're delightful, I'm told,' says Juan, whose adequate English garners him further points. 'I've not been there myself. We usually take our holidays in Cannes.'

I'm surprised, I must say. One doesn't as a rule imagine Spaniards taking holidays – one pictures them in fact carrying trays for others. ('*Dos sangrias*, Pedro. Chop chop.')

'Well done,' I say. 'A small break for myself and the lady wife after our researches in Essential Spain. You'll not have been there, I don't suppose. A hundred years off the beaten track. The superstitious festivals. The ceremonial spearing of the goat. The butcher's lady as the Virgin Mary. I'll not go further. Where was I?'

'You're a busy man,' says Mrs Root.

'So I am, so I am.'

'So how can I help you?' asks Juan.

'The fact is I represent Branson. You'll have heard of him, no doubt. May have seen him on TV. May have seen me, come to that. The Jean Pierre Foucault show. A French job. He's by no means as stupid as he looks. I'm referring to Branson. On his behalf I'm on the *qui vive* here for cashed up companies which might slot in with one of his.. You're in furniture, I gather? Right. A tour of the factory, if you wouldn't mind. Depending on what I see we might do business. Let's go. Lead on McJuan!'

The Managing Director is impressed, can smell a Euro-deal no doubt, escorts us to the shop floor where I splash encouragement around, slap a few backs bent double over lathes.

'Well done, Pedro. Keep up the good work.'

I'm on the look-out for *mañana*-like work habits which, if brought to Britain, could pervert factory practices on a Hounslow industrial estate.

'Head down, Antonio. Splendid girl, your sister, from all I hear.'

I must go down to the sea again. *En route* to the so-called Balearics for a sunshine break, and already dressed in holiday mode, I research a furniture factory. I check with the MD that they're geared up for 1992. We'll not want the *mañana* attitude in British boardrooms.

Mrs Root is impressed by the goods on offer. She tries out settees, examines a coffee-table fashioned in the manner of a porpoise standing on its tail, opens up a cocktail cabinet shaped like an elephant with a little Indian on top, lifts the little Indian by his turban to reveal bottles and glasses within.

'This is ever so tasteful, Henry,' she says. 'Michael and Mary Parkinson would appreciate a cocktail cabinet like this.'

'I dare say they would, Mrs Root,' I say. 'We're not on a shopping trip, however. Right – I've seen enough. We'll be off now, Juan. You'll be hearing from myself or Branson shortly.'

Juan – sensing a considerable order in the offing – surprises me at this point by suggesting lunch *al fresco* with himself and a handful of senior personnel. I'm about to demur – squid, I imagine, if not worse – when I see this as a chance to research the lunchtime blow-out followed by the long *siesta*.

'This will be telling, Mrs Root. It will sink them, mark my words. I'll not want to involve Branson with Spaniards customarily on their backs between three and eight p.m. He had enough trouble with the fat one in a dress.'

'Boy George, Henry?'

'She's the one, Mrs Root. Well done. Stay off trhe regional *cuisine*, that's my advice.'

We all depart together for the local yacht club. Vast quantities of food and wine are taken – by Juan and his team, at least. Mrs Root and I consume more moderately.

The *al fresco* lunchtime blow-out: *gambas a la plancha*, a flan for afters and a choice of wine. Instructed by me, Mrs Root imbibes with moderation. I'll be all right. I've a head like a rock. Our hosts – the Chairman, the MD, the dizzy little PR girl – will be out for the afternoon.

The meal completed, Juan and his team announce that it's time to return to work.

'This will be telling, Mrs Root. It will be the long *siesta* now. You'll see. They'll crash like ninepins, mark my words.'

There must have been more in the *vino tinto* than I suspected. The next thing I know I wake up in reception next to Mrs Root, the two of us stretched out on a desk, toes up like medieval lovers on a tomb. Not our fault. The Spanish should be more careful with what they offer British punters over lunch. I'll warn Branson of this on my return.

Once on our feet, we drive to Valencia harbour, where I locate the booking-hall for the so-called Balearics. I address myself to a uniformed *hombre* behind a glass partition.

'Two to the Balearics, my good man, plus car.'

'*Si señor.* Majorca, Ibiza or Menorca?'

'That's right. They'll do.'

'Which one, *señor?*'

'The Balearics, Pedro, We've got one here, Mrs Root.'

The fellow's a Catalan, that's my guess, but I sort him out eventually, purchase tickets for Ibiza, Menorca and Majorca, which, as I explain to Pedro, constitute the Balearics.

We find our cabin, are momentarily disconcerted to discover that we're sharing it with another couple, and a Spanish one at that.

'We've drawn the short straw here, Mrs Root. Spanish, do you see? Keep an eye on the roughage. Your first trip abroad, is it, Pedro?'

Pedro says it is indeed his first trip to the Balearics, so I ask what takes him there.

'Got a small business, have you? A souvenir shop perhaps? A little tourist trap? Hats for the Germans or something of that sort? Nothing wrong with that. Glad you chaps are able to make a living now. You've a lot to thank the General for.'

'In fact we're going there on holiday,' Pedro says.

'There's a turn-up, Mrs Root. Our second in a day in this regard. Juan at the factory takes an annual general, you'll recall. They're all at it, it seems. Nothing wrong with that, I suppose. You could say its progress of a sort. Well done, Pedro. Don't stay out in the sun too long – and stick to the British *cuisine*, that's my advice.'

I then organise the sleeping arrangements, draw up a schedule for the use of the toilet and shower facilities.

Tuesday, 25th June 1991

We arrive in the Balearics, head for San Antonio Abad where we book in at the Hotel Marco Polo.

'This is agreeable, Mrs Root. We've fallen on our feet. They have amenities here that the Cunard Hotel, Hammersmith would be proud of, to say nothing of an *autopiste* Novotel.'

We set off to investigate the town and beaches. I'm quite impressed. There is an abundance of Watney's pubs and fish and chip shops advertising 'Decent English Food'. On the beach jolly English grannies sunbathe in their corsets, later tuck their skirts into their pink ballooning knickers and wade, squealing, into the sea.

In the Balearics. Mrs Root and I stroll through the agreeable holiday resort of San Antonio. Once a sleepy little fishing village, but now 'the times they are a-changing'. (Dylan Thomas, was it?) Thanks to the British, there's something for everyone – novelty shops, a fat woman dispensing candyfloss, Cannon and Ball in cabaret. Nothing wrong with that. It could be Margate.

'This is pleasant, Mrs Root.'

'It wouldn't be where I'd choose to take a holiday, Henry.'

'No need to scoff, Mrs Root. The simple pleasures of simple folk. They have leisure facilities here that Blackpool would be proud of. Not that I've ever been to Blackpool, I'm glad to say.'

'I wasn't going to scoff, Henry. I did read somewhere, though, that British holiday-makers don't always behave themselves.'

'A pardonable excess of the Falklands spirit, Mrs Root. Plus the Spanish licensing laws are in large part responsible for an outbreak of undue high spirits – throwing yomping Swedes into empty swimming pools and so forth. The British are unaccustomed to drinking all day in the sun. The Spanish should tighten their licensing laws, which, no doubt, they'll be obliged to do post-1992. Care for a drink, Mrs Root?'

Mrs Root seems surprised. 'Goodness, Henry,' she says. 'It's only half past ten.'

'We're working, Mrs Root.'

As luck would have it, we've paused outside an agreeable little pub, aptly named the Francis Drake – Tudor accoutrements, tankards, a likeness on its walls of the Armada turning turtle. It's empty except for mine host and a middle-aged English customer in a 'kiss-me-quick' hat. I try to avoid him, not wishing to be seen with a suburban type like this, but he greets us with a volley of saloon bar *bonhomie*.

'Oh oh. Look what the cat dragged in!' he cries. 'Don't mind me. Nobby Norris. From Woking. How do you do?'

Outside Ye Olde Francis Drake, Nobby Norris, a retired insurance salesman from Woking, foolishly mistakes me for a tourist! And look at him! With legs like that, I'd keep my trousers on.

I blanch, frankly, look round to see if I'm being observed in proximity to a type like this, a caricature of the worst sort of English-man, the kind that gives us a bad image on the Continent. We're

unobserved, so I introduce myself and Mrs Root – somewhat formally
– and briefly shake the fellow's hand.

'Henry Root. Wet Fish. And this is the lady wife, Muriel.'

'Wet fish eh? No wonder the cat dragged you in!' The fool cackles
with laughter. 'Having a good holiday, are you?'

I let him have it. '*Holiday*! We've got one here, Mrs Root. *Holiday*!
Do I look like a man on holiday? Nothing of the sort, Rodney. . . .'

'Nobby.'

'I can see that. No, we're here in Majorca *in re* 1992. . . .'

'Ibiza, Henry,' says Mrs Root.

'If you say so, Mrs Root. You've got the map. Researching for the
BBC and Lord Weidenfeld of Nicolson.'

Nobby's taken aback, I'm glad to say, suspends his vile suburban
cackling for the moment. 'My mistake. What will it be, then?'

'Two sherry wines, thank you, Rodney. You can get it here, you
know.'

I move from the bar, place myself on an upturned powder keg
fashioned as a seat. To my displeasure, Mrs Root now addresses the
vulgar oaf.

'Are you on holiday, Nobby?'

'No, I live here, for my sins.'

'That must be nice,' says Mrs Root.

I take the woman to one side. 'Don't encourage the man, for
goodness' sake. Frightful type. Don't know why he left Woking. No
attempt to blend. No respect for the indigenous *mores*. His days will
be numbered post-1992.'

It's too late. There's no stopping the idiot now.

'Mind you, if it wasn't for the weather I'd have stayed in Woking.
Still – can't complain. The booze is cheap, there's nothing wrong with
Johnnie Spaniard if you leave him alone and I can get the *Daily
Telegraph*.'

I conceal my own copy of the *Telegraph* under my powder keg.

'You're a *Telegraph* man I take it, Henry?'

'Certainly not! I've read the *Guardian* all my life!'

Mrs Root then asks the idiot whether he speaks Spanish.

'Now there's a funny thing, Muriel,' he says. 'May I call you
Muriel? I've been living here for twenty years and they still can't
understand me. Yesterday in the supermarket I wanted some eggs. I
flapped my arms and went "cluck cluck". They gave me toilet rolls.
They're funny people, the Spanish.'

He's quite cast down, I'm glad to say, silent for the moment at the
memory, allowing Mrs Root, who has been reading a guidebook on
the Balearics bought in a *kiosko* on the ferry, to change the subject.

'It says here, Henry, that Salinas is the nicest beach on the island.
Don't you think we ought to see it?'

Nobby, now recovered, interrupts again. 'Salinas? I'd steer clear of that, if I were you. Full of trendies. The self-appointed in-crowd. Loafers. Hippies. The so-called smart set. I've not been there myself, of course.'

'I'm not surprised,' I say. 'We'll see for ourselves, I think. Come along, Mrs Root.'

Nobby won't give up. As we leave the bar, he calls out after us.

'See you tonight then, Henry?'

'Not if I see you first, Rodney!' I riposte. 'What a frightful type, Mrs Root. We'll not want to be seen with him again. There'll be no place for him in the New Europe, that's for sure. Follow me. We're off to Salinas.'

We're out in the street, we've put fifty yards between us and the Francis Drake, when Nobby catches up with us.

'Hang on, Henry,' he shouts. 'Not so fast. You left your *Daily Telegraph* behind.'

I roll it up and whack him hard – a warning shot between the eyes – feel better after that. We return to our hotel, attire ourselves as per a beach where the in-crowd rendezvous – myself in floral shorts from Peter Jones, socks by Lacoste, sandals by Dolcis (the Esher branch), Mrs Root in something from Oxford Street for the larger woman – and sally forth once more, stopping on the way at a novelty shop, in which I purchase a lilo fashioned after the manner of an inflatable shark, previously admired on San Antonio's beach.

We arrive at Salinas, park the car and head for where the jet set muster.

Every picture tells a story, they say. Here's an exception.

'This is agreeable, Mrs Root. We'll sit . . . Jumping Jesus! What's this?'

We're in Sodom by the sea, we're confronted on all sides by a shameless mix of snake-thin naked beach boys and Swedish 'models' oiling one another's buttery ballooning buttocks. I avert my eyes, clutch my inflatable shark.

'Tell me I'm dreaming, Mrs Root.'

'It's just young people enjoying themselves, Henry,' she says.

'I'll tell you what it is, Mrs Root. It's hedonism off the leash. We'll not want that in Bournemouth.'

'Come on Henry,' the woman says. 'You sound just like Nobby. What's wrong with it?'

'Everything, Mrs Root. Unrepressed behaviour. Sensuality out of control. Unrestrained vulgarity.'

She won't concede. 'An excess of holiday spirit, Henry. You liked San Antonio, and that was vulgar.'

She understands nothing. 'That was *British* vulgarity, Mrs Root. Perfectly healthy. Nothing explicit below the belt. This is Continental vulgarity, which is an entirely different matter. It's disgusting, frankly.'

I decide notwithstanding – and for the sake of my research – to stick it out. I instruct Mrs Root to follow me, looking neither to left nor right. We find a place for two, position ourselves cheek by jowl between unnaturally dark-skinned Continental elements. Mrs Root makes herself comfortable, suggests that I remove my socks and sandals.

'Not at the moment, thank you, Mrs Root. I may take a paddle later.'

Mrs Root produces a copy of *Woman's Weekly* – brought from Esher, I wouldn't wonder (there are times when the woman lets me down) – while I struggle to restrain the shark, which seems to have taken on a life of its own, at one moment cannoning off the – excuse me – naked bosoms of the Swedish 'model' to my left. I lose confidence in the shark, attempt to deflate it by withdrawal of a toggle with my teeth. It emits a low intestinal moan, which causes Mrs Root to address the 'model' on her right.

'It's his wind,' she explains. 'He's a martyr to his tummy.'

'Never mind my wind, Mrs Root. . . . Jumping Jesus, what's that?!'

A stone nude Negro is padding slowly like a ballet man along the beach, followed by a retinue of naked fairies. The awe with which he's greeted suggests he's the heavy-centre of the in-set. I'm not impressed.

'What does he think he looks like?' I say to Mrs Root.

'I think he looks beautiful,' says Mrs Root. 'I expect they pay him to sit on the beach and look good.'

'Let's hope he doesn't take his business to Bournemouth, that's all I can say. Majorca indeed. You can keep it. The punters should be warned.'

'Ibiza, Henry,' says Mrs Root.

'There too, I wouldn't wonder. I've seen enough. It's time to leave. Come along, Mrs Root.'

I bury the shark's remains under a mound of sand and head towards the exit. We're almost there when the topless 'model' who's been posing next to Mrs Root accosts me from behind.

'Excuse me, *señor*,' she says. 'You left your shark behind.'

'It's not mine, madam,' I say. I point to the naked negro with the entourage of faires. 'I think it's his.'

She seems quite startled. 'It belongs to Zorka the Island God?' she says.

I've cooked his goose. I've put him back to square one socially.

'In that case I must get one too,' she says. '*Adíos, señor.* I hope your wind improves.' She dances back along the beach with a happy cry of 'Look at my shark everyone!'

'Like sheep,' I explain to Mrs Root. 'Just because the so-called Island God has a shark they all want one. If he donned a "kiss-me-quick" hat and hired a pedalo they'd follow suit.'

'He has,' says Mrs Root, 'and they have.'

In the evening we drive into Ibiza town, place ourselves – for research purposes – outside a trendy bar. Eccentrically dressed young people jostle to left and right. Zulu music deafens us in either ear.

'Depravity, Mrs Root,' I say. 'Half of them look like girls.'

Shark ahoy! Once it's inflated, I'll have some fun with this, surprise the lass on my right, perhaps, with some nautical manoeuvres they didn't include in *Jaws.* Some don't blend with the *à la mode.* I do.

'That's because half of them are girls,' says Mrs Root.

'If you say so, Mrs Root. What my pal the Judge would say I do not know. On drugs most of them, I wouldn't wonder. Pedro! *An otra piña colada por favor!*'

'Don't you think you've had enough, Henry?'

'Don't fuss, Mrs Root. Head like a rock. Naval man. *Olé*! I could drink this lot . . . Goats and monkeys! Look what the cat's dragged in!'

Zorka the Island God has entered with his entourage, wearing a diaphanous negligée of sorts over a bejewelled *cache-sexe*. If he was wearing wings he'd resemble King Oberon in the thing by old Bill Shakespeare with the other one – Tanya, was it? – and his retinue of fairies.

'It's that chap from the beach,' says Mrs Root. 'Doesn't he look nice?'

'*Nice*, Mrs Root? He's wearing a lady's nightdress. He'd better not speak to me, that's all I can say. I'm disappointed, frankly. They've sold out, do you see?'

'Who's sold out, Henry?'

'The Spanish, Mrs Root. They've bargained their history away for a few pesetas, stood idly by as their once proud country is transformed into a paradise for perverts. Look at her.'

'Who, Henry?'

'Her over there. The beshawled peasant lady sitting on her porch. Probably owns three hotels and a filling station, last went to church in 1958. The goat in her lounge-room will have been replaced by a cocktail cabinet fashioned in the manner of an elephant with a little Indian on top. Mark my words.'

'She seems contented enough, Henry.'

'So would you, Mrs Root, if you owned three hotels and a filling station. If there's one thing I can't stand, however, it's people who lack the courage of their convictions, who'll be blown hither and thither by whatever's *au courant*.'

I now notice that Zorka the so-called Island God is looking in our direction. He'd better not speak to me. He does.

'Hey,' he cries. 'What's happening? You're the fellow with the shark! Care to join us?'

Not so odd, I suppose. Takes one to know one. Different in-crowds – Zorka presides here in Majorca, I in Esher – otherwise peas in a pod. I move across to my pal Zorka's table, sit on a chair offered by one of his entourage. I play it cool.

'The drinks are on me,' I shout. 'No! I insist. Pedro! One of the same for my young friends. Chop chop!'

'What about your wife?' says Zorka.

'What about her?'

'Wouldn't she like to join us?'

He gets up and fetches Mrs Root. She'll let herself down, but never mind. I'm not the sort who disowns his wife in public. The drinks arrive, the young folk thank me. I modestly raise a hand.

'Please. Hussey will pay. It's down to the BBC.'

The trendies are impressed. 'The BBC?' says one of them who, I notice, isn't wearing any trousers. Nothing wrong with that. Hot night. Young people on holiday. Live and let live.

'That's right,' I say. 'A major TV series fronted by myself. Henry Root. Wet Fish. My card.'

I hand my card to Zorka, who tucks it away in his bejewelled *cache-sexe*. Meanwhile, trendy elements at the adjoining table exchange the news that I represent the BBC. Several get up and join our party.

'The series,' I say, 'will deal with Europe post-1992. That's why I'm here. Research. I'll be reporting back to the Prime Minister.'

My audience is impressed. I can see that at the edges of our group young people are exchanging the name of the British PM, are miming a man in a suit, a square head, a straight face. Our party expands.

'I've done France and Belgium so far. In France I appeared to effect on the Foucault show. Thirty million viewers.'

An excited buzz goes round the bar. ('Good *gracias*! Thirty million viewers!') Our group expands again.

Al fresco in the evening, the beautiful people hang on my every word. I have at my fingertips the latest lingo – a special skill of mine. 'What's new, pussycat? She loves you, yeah yeah yeah.' I'll have a job to shake them off.

'Pedro! *Treinta mas piña coladas, por favor.* I was less impressed by Brussels, however. Walloons for the most part.'

There is general agreement among my young friends. They nod their heads, mime fat men, mutter that they're all Walloons in Brussels. Two fat businessmen in suits get up and leave. Just as well. They didn't fit in, failed abjectly to go with the flow.

'Early night, Grandpa?' I say to their retreating backs. I continue with my story. 'However, I did meet Sir Brittan.'

The news that Sir Brittan's in must spread like wildfire round the immediate environs. We're shortly joined by another dozen or so young people.

'A major enterprise, as I say. The BBC has already allocated a large chunk of next year's budget. Supply and demand, back to back, revolving credit. . . .'

At the next-door bar two girls dancing on a tabletop stop in mid-routine, exchange the news. ('Back-to-back, revolving credit. . . .') They join our party.

'There'll be residuals, of course. Repeats, T-shirts, franchises, a pop-up book for Lord Weidenfeld of Nicolson.'

This puts the cap on it, it seems. In a nearby doorway a street addict, cuddling an inflatable shark, pummels his pal awake and passes on the news. ('Lord Weidenfeld's in.') They struggle to their feet and join my party. They hit it off with Mrs Root, admire her trouser suit.

'Cool running,' I say. 'Nothing wrong with the occasional smoke. Live and let live.' I'm feeling good. 'Where to now, then? The night is young.'

My pal Zorka the Island God suggests that we move on to Pacha, a local discothèque.

'Dancing, is it? The rumba? The *paso doble*? House music, perhaps? The Balearic beat? I'm on. Let's go. *Olé!*'

I'm a Pied Piper to the island's young folk. They follow me to Pacha, collecting others as we go. ('Revolving credit . . . back-to-back . . . Lord Weidenfeld of Nicolson . . . Sir Brittan's in . . . Hussey will pay.')

We arrive at Pacha – an agreeable open-air *palais de danse* – quickly make our presence felt. The word gets round that the drinks are on the BBC ('*El Duc de Hussey*, he pay . . .') I dance with Zorka on a rostrum, young folk cheer. I tap on the window of the disc jockey's cubicle, instruct him in the old favourites.

'You've Dame Lynn, have you? Weee-ll meeeeet ag-aain, don't know where, don't know whe-eeen.' He doesn't know it. 'Or Iglesias, if you prefer? The little Spaniard?' I dance vigorously, sign a bill presented to me as I execute a pirouette.

I teach my new young friends the Lambeth Walk. As the sun rises in the east I lead a snaking conga out of Pacha towards Ibiza Town,

Music maestro please! In Pacha, the fashionable local *palais*, I dance on a podium, encouraged by my new young friends. The twist, is it? Zorka the Island God, astern, attempts to ape my movements. 'Pop of the Tops, is it?' someone cries. She goes head first into a parking bollard.

through the deserted streets and down to the harbour, where a solitary fisherman mends his nets. ('If you come down Lambeth Way, any evening, any day. . . .you'll find us all, dooo-ing the Lambeth Walk. . . .Oi!!')

Enough's enough. I know when to take my leave. I take a sharp turn to the left, conga off with Mrs Root, allowing my young friends to snake away into the distance, singing and dancing happily ('Everything bright and breezy. . . .do as you darn well pleeee-zy!') I'd made my point, I think.

Back in our hotel suite, I rumba out of the bathroom, join Mrs Root, who is already in bed, reading her picture-book.

'You shouldn't leap to conclusions, Mrs Root,' I say. 'Pass judgement just because a fellow wears a dress. Did you see how those young people took to me?'

'I'd look in your wallet if I was you, Henry,' says Mrs Root.

To accommodate her, I fetch my wallet and look inside. My cash and credit facilities are, as I thought, intact.

'There you are, Mrs Root. I'd trust those . . . Jumping Jesus! What's this?'

I'd come across Pacha's bill, signed by myself in mid-step on the dance floor. I must have bought champagne for eighty people.

I'm a Pied Piper to the island's young folk. As dawn comes up, I lead them in a snaking conga out of Pacha and down to the harbour, where a solitary fisherman mends his nets.

CHAPTER EIGHT

Arrivederci Roma

Saturday, 29th June 1991

Three days have passed. We've left Majorca, I'm glad to say, there-after sticking to the *autopiste* as we drive through France looking neither to right nor left (we've done France, have nothing else to learn) and head towards Italy – the nadir of my research. As we reach the Italian border, I slip the theme from *The Godfather* into the Jaguar's cassette facility. I hum along, then elucidate *in re* Italy for Mrs Root.

'Italy, Mrs Root. Got to face it some time. Our sternest test. Instability off the leash. Your average Italian is quite unsocialised, his attitude being – you'll pardon my French, Mrs Root – "Up yours, Giacometti, I'm all right."'

As if to illustrate my point, an overtaking Fiat causes me to take sudden evasive action, its excitable little driver thanking me for my life-saving, cobra-quick reactions with a volley of Italian insults.

'What did I tell you, Mrs Root? Traffic disputes, you'll find, are traditionally settled by an exchange of small-arms fire. Plus, and further, your little Italian is historically ungovernable, small warring parties stapled together in a hurry – the Guelphs and Ghibbelines, was it? We'll meet them later, I've no doubt – the mix as volatile as gelignite in a microwave.'

'It's a toss-up which is more corrupt, business or politics – not that politics is governance as we'd recognise the term. They have one MP, I've heard, who, to drum up business on the hustings, consistently poses on Page Three and elsewhere in the buff. We'll not want that in the Mother of Parliaments, Mrs Root, we'll not want Tory ladies in the buff, either on the front bench or, at the annual conference by the sea, waltzing thus with old Lord Whitelaw and other provincial butterballs. In due course, I may well quiz this lady as to her intentions. Madame Cicciolina, if I'm not mistaken. Not a pleasant job, but someone's got to do it. Your Italian's first loyalty is towards himself, thereafter to his family. Your Italian has an unhealthy respect for family values.'

'That's odd, Henry.'

'What's odd, Mrs Root?'

'Well, family values – they're normally thought to be a good thing, the cornerstone of morality etc. How can respect for the family be a bad thing?'

'You've got me there, Mrs Root. I'm temporarily nonplussed. Can't for the moment get my brain round this apparent paradox. I'll puzzle it out, give you the answer in a jiffy.'

We drive on, heading south towards Rome, see a signpost to Milan.

'Milan, Mrs Root. We ought to cover it. The centre of the fashion industry, I'm told.'

We leave the *autopiste*, enter Milan, park the car near the Duomo, whatever that might be, locate a coffee shop. I summon up a waiter, ask him whether they do *cappuccino*. Apparently they do. They've learnt something from the Spanish, it seems. I eye the waiter warily, rebuke Mrs Root for smiling at him.

'Don't encourage the man, Mrs Root. As I've said before, the Italian male poses a constant threat to the respectable Englishwoman. The latest laboratory tests show that the Italian male thinks about it every thirty seconds. Happily, I shall be at your side and armed. A blow to the back of the neck with a rolled-up copy of the *Telegraph* and your little Italian goes down like an ox in an abattoir. All front, do you see?'

Mrs Root is disposed to give me an argument, it seems. 'That may be true, Henry, but they are very good-looking. And so are the women. Look at her. She's ever so beautiful.'

'Probably English, Mrs Root. The average Italian girl is quite pretty up to the age of eighteen, but within six months of returning from her honeymoon she looks like Pavarotti. It's the pasta, do you see? It has been estimated that the average Italian consumes in one calendar year four and a half miles of spaghetti. Which is why your

A chic shopping complex in Milan – the city famous for its hats. That's as may be. What's not so well known is that 'Lord' Ted Dexter was born in Milan and played his early cricket there for a local club. When Dexter was made Captain of England, a non-denominational service of thanksgiving was held in Milan Cathedral (Dexter is Church of England).

local buck prefers lardy English girls on holiday, offering themselves arse-up over dry-stone walls. You'll excuse my French.'

'If you say so, Henry.'

'I'll tell you more, Mrs Root. The problems for your little Italian Romeo start when trying to form a connection with an Italian girl. First he has to meet her extended family and kitchen utensils. He will be expected to have dinner with her parents, grandparents, uncles, aunts, cousins, brothers and sisters and to compliment her mother on the meatballs. After supper the young couple, having nowhere to go in private, are compelled to advance the liaison on the back seat of a parked car. I've heard it said that cars parked in Italian streets bob up and down like corks in a torrent. Where did we leave the Jaguar? We'll not want liaisons on the All-Bran.'

'It's quite safe, Henry. I can see it from here.'

'Well done, woman. Well – that's enough of that. We've done Milan. Onwards!'

Mrs Root seems surprised. 'Already, Henry? We've only just arrived. The shops look lovely. Couldn't we do some shopping?'

'No time for that, Mrs Root. There's work to be done. We're not here to enjoy ourselves.'

'I know that, Henry. But they do have some lovely things. And everyone looks so smart. So elegant. And confident.'

'A mirage, Mrs Root. A triumph of style over content – mere window-dressing. Fashion and frivolity papering over a moral vacuum. Italy is a rose garden built on a cesspit. Lilies that fester and so forth. It's madness. Anarchy. Come! We've work to do.'

We leave the café, walk back towards the car. On the way I have to chivvy Mrs Root, who constantly pauses outside shops. Not yards from where the car is parked, my eye is caught by rather a natty panama hat in the window of a gentleman's outfitters. I enter and purchase it. It suits me well.

'What's your ruling, Mrs Root? Smart, do you think?'

'It's lovely, Henry.'

We leave Milan, continue south. I'm in good spirits. I offer a verse or two of 'Volare' as per the little American crooner, Dean Martin, is it? Suddenly it hits me.

'I have it, Mrs Root. The answer to your problem. I told you I'd puzzle it out.'

'What problem, Henry?' says Mrs Root, who seems a little glum, I don't know why.

'The apparent paradox as to your Italian's respect for the family on one hand and his contempt for law and order on the other. There's nothing wrong with the nuclear unit, do you see – the bedrock, as you say, of traditional morality – but the Italian typically exaggerates the concept, having an unhealthy respect for the *extended* family, putting its interests before those of the community as a whole. No good can come of that. The origins of some family vendettas are lost in the mists of time. Romeo and Juliet, was it? Lord Montague and Capulet? In some areas, mainly to the south, it is not unusual to find a family of forty all living under the same roof – uncles, great-grandfathers, distant cousins, fat women in the kitchen – all carrying shotguns. That can't be right. Sooner rather than later, the upcoming generation should tip their elders into the street or lock them in the madhouse. A family should be at odds with itself. I myself, as you know, took over the family whelk stall from my grandfather Henry "Cannonball" Root, at the business end of a writ. He had to laugh, was still laughing when I put him in the pokey. Hence your Mafia.'

'The Mafia, Henry? I hope we don't meet them.'

'Unavoidable, woman. Your Italian has taken his family way of doing things into organised crime. Having no respect for central government, he makes his bones over the meatballs, kisses a goat's private parts and then shoots the man next door. We'll not want that in Esher.'

'We certainly won't, Henry.'

'Already your Italian has taken his family way of doing things to the United States. Your American Cosa Nostra is unable to pass a patch of wet cement without tipping someone into it. Look what happened to Jimmy Hoffa. Under a concrete pylon propping up a baseball stadium. We don't want that in England. Tempting as it may be, we don't want Bernie Grant six feet under a building site at the whim of some moustachioed Don.'

We bowl along the *autopiste*, see a signpost to Bologna.

'Bologna, Mrs Root. This could be appertaining. Sums up the central paradox of Italy, highlights the madness, do you see? A Communist stronghold here in the affluent North. Not yards from where Ferraris are made a Bolshevik in braces presides in the town hall. Yet in the poverty-stricken South, where it's three to the shirt and the outside bucket, the populace is happy to have their affairs controlled by the afore-mentioned dapper men in handstitched underwear carrying violin cases. What do you make of that, Mrs Root?'

'It's a paradox, Henry.'

'We'll stop off and see the mayor. Catch him with his goats.'

We take the exit for Bologna, enter the city and park the car in a broken-down old square known as the Piazza Maggiore, where Mayor

In Bologna's celebrated old Piazza Maggiore, two veiled Muslim ladies in search of Mecca. They're in the wrong neck of the woods entirely.

Imbeni has his office. We climb a worn old staircase which should have been demolished centuries ago, enter the reception hall.

'We'll catch him in his office,' I explain to Mrs Root. 'Our last chance to see a type like him – the representative of a dying breed. A threatened species. A dinosaurus. A blue whale deprived of its political plankton, beached by the tide of history. A fish out of water.'

'The whale isn't a fish, Henry,' says Mrs Root, who has recently become a touch disputatious for a woman. A habit she picked up in France, I fear.

'A red herring, if you prefer. My point holds, nonetheless.'

I knuckle the reception desk, introduce myself to a lass on the Mayor's staff.

'*Bon tarde, señorita.* Henry Root. Wet Fish. A quick word with the Mayor, if you'd be so kind.'

The lass seems baffled, so I explain further.

'Travelling through Europe on behalf of the BBC. Planning a Festival of European Culture – thought His Worship might measure up in a spaghetti tent. Him and his goat.'

The lass on reception examines my card, puts a call through to His Worship's office.

'He'll be a grizzled crop-haired peasant,' I explain to Mrs Root. 'With hands like hams and opinions as outdated as his trousers. We'd better dress down, we don't want to embarrass him. You'll be all right. I'll remove my hat.'

The lass on reception now tells us that the Mayor is very busy at the moment but might be able to give me a few minutes between appointments.

Renzo Ibini, the Communist Mayor of Bolgona, models his new Armani suit at a congress of European haberdashers. We'll not want types like him contesting Billericay North.

'We're all busy, my dear,' I riposte. 'It is my intention to be out of Italy by the day after tomorrow, so if you could ask His Worship to leave milking the goats till later, I'd be much obliged.'

That does the trick. The Mayor's secretary shortly arrives and escorts us to his office. I am immediately put somewhat on the back foot by the fact that he is an expensively dressed man, evincing suspect charm.

'If he's a Communist,' I observe to Mrs Root, 'I'd hate to meet the Conservatives.'

'Forgive me,' His Worship says. 'I have another meeting soon, so I can only give you a few minutes. How can I help you exactly?'

I put the fellow at his ease. 'Don't mention it, Your Worship. Fact is I can't stay long myself. Just passing through on the way to Rome. I hope to be out of Italy by the day after tomorrow. As it happens, I expected to find you packing.'

The fellow seems baffled by my little joke. He's obviously not as sophisticated as he'd like to think, unacquainted at least with under-stated English irony.

'Just ribbing you, Your Worship. I was referring to the golden handshake. A carriage clock at least for twenty years loyal service to the Party. Then off to Moscow – expenses paid – and a *dacha* by the Baltic. The party's over for you lot, isn't it? Thanks to our own Mrs Thatcher, the map of Europe has been radically altered in the last two years. The tide of history has left people of your persuasion – Communists, Trots, Marxists, whatever – up the creek without a paddle.'

The Mayor takes it on the chin – I'll say that for him – gives me a charming smile, but is disposed to dispute the point. He goes so far as to tell me that I'm misinformed, says such indeed to a reader of the *Daily Telegraph*! I manage not to laugh.

'For one thing,' he says, 'I'm not a Marxist. In Italy, the Com-munist Party has never followed the Russian model. Here we have always believed in democracy and free elections.'

At this point a dapper assistant glides in and informs His Worship that he must shortly leave for his next appointment.

'Yes, yes,' he says, brushing the fellow aside. He may be a Com-munist, but he knows what my friend Paul Johnson would call a political heavyweight when he sees one. 'You must understand, Mr Root, that after the war, after the Fascist regime of Mussolini, many people here welcomed Communism with open arms. It meant free-dom, not repression. The Party has never imposed state control on industry or farming. Private property has been respected.'

The Mayor's factotum, who won't be shaken off, now insists that he puts on his chain of office prior to the next appointment.

'Bologna,' he continues, 'has been a Communist stronghold since the war and the people here have enjoyed prosperity and – most importantly in Italy, perhaps – political stability. My approach has always been to move with the times, to adapt to changing circumstances and, since there is no longer an unacceptable contrast between the rich and the poor, I and my Party reflect this in our policies. In many ways you could say that I am to the right of the British Labour Party!'

It's my turn to be baffled. I struggle to get my brain round this unexpected concept. I turn to Mrs Root.

'We've got one here, Mrs Root. A recruit to the Liberal Democrats in the Italian Communist Party. We come all this way and what do we find? Shirley Williams. It's worse than I expected.'

'I've always liked Shirley Williams,' says Mrs Root. 'She's ever so natural. Not at all stuck-up.'

And this somewhat less-than-telling contribution is the last shot on our side in what has been a most interesting political discussion. The Mayor says that it's been a pleasure talking to me but he must now go to his next appointment. We're ushered out, return down the stairs to the Piazza Maggiore.

'What a charming man,' says Mrs Root.

Women are easily deceived, not having our experience of the hard political realities.

'Too charming, Mrs Root. He's not endangered, do you see? Far from it. He's evolved, adapted – as he had the front to admit himself. Someone slightly to the left of centre who could win elections. A Bolshevik with ballot-box appeal. We'll not want that coming through the Channel Tunnel. He'll need watching.'

Mrs Root, I fear, seems to have been hypnotised by the fellow's wafer-thin allure.

'I don't think you need worry, Henry,' she says. 'His appeal is very Italian – if you know what I mean. It's hard to imagine anyone as attractive as that in British politics.'

I'm frankly scandalised. 'What you're saying verges on the blasphemous, woman! The man is as slippery as an eel. A dandy. An afternoon man. You could hire him out to dance with older women at a *palais*. I mean, your squat, old-time Bolshevik in a suit stitched together from industrial sacking – you knew where you stood with him.'

A thought suddenly occurs. 'I wonder where he got his shoes?'

No sooner said than we happen to pass a gentlemen's shoe shop with, in the window, a pair identical to His Worship's. I slip inside and purchase them. In these, and in my hat from Milan, I look the part, unless I'm much mistaken. I blend. There's little I can do about Mrs Root, I fear. Sad what happens to women.

In no time we're back on the road, driving south to Rome. I wear my hat at an Italian angle, my gestures have become enlarged. I begin to find that I can communicate adequately – and insultingly – with the natives without recourse to English. I spar like a gladiator with the traffic. '*Bastardo*! Up yours, Giacometti!' We pass a signpost indicating that Florence is to our left.

'Florence, Henry!' cries Mrs Root. 'They've got ever so much art there, I believe. Untold treasures and so forth. Can't we stop?'

Florence's Opera House from the *auto-piste*. The best place to see it from in my opinion. Pavarotti, the world-famous tenor, is quite un-appreciated in Florence, where he was born, and has never been invited to appear there in any of his great operatic roles. He is known here only for his album 'Pavarotti Sings Cole Porter', in which he is backed by James Last and his Alpine Orchestra.

I quickly put the lid on that.

'Art, Mrs Root? Nothing wrong with it in its place – which is in the vault of a bank standing security against your Glaxo shares.'

She's keen to dispute the point. The woman's getting out of hand.

'Well,' she says, 'I think it would be lovely to live among so much beauty.'

'Bad for the character, Mrs Root. Look at your Italian. Bruised by culture, by an excess of history at every turn. Expose an Englishman to too much pottery and his brain rots. Keats, was it? "Ode to an Urn"? The Spanish Steps? "Beauty is truth, truth beauty" and so forth? Drowned in the Hellespont and I'm not surprised. Anyway, we'll get enough of that in Rome – the Appian Way, the Parthian Shot, the Pyrrhic Victory – we'll get enveloped if we don't watch out. Hercules and the Wooden Horse of Troy. Penelope and her chastity belt. Paris, Achilles sulking in his tent, the one with no arms – Aphrodite, was it? Agamemnon. Good name for a cat, if you ask me.'

Mrs Root consults her guidebook.

'That's Greek, Henry.'

'You're telling me, Mrs Root.'

Mrs Root continues to read her guidebook, shortly offers further redundant information.

'We're passing through Tuscany,' she says.

'I'm delighted to hear it, Mrs Root,' I say. 'We'll not stop here. The hills are lousy with thin-legged literary types from England. Sir Acton, the old aesthete in his *doge*. Rumpole of the Bailey quoting Wordsworth.'

As dusk approaches we arrive at the outskirts of Rome.

'The eternal city, Mrs Root. This won't take long.'

I swerve confidently across a lane of traffic, shout defiantly at indignant, honking Romans and take an exit for the city centre. As we look across at the twilit, panoramic view, I further educate Mrs Root.

'Those will be the seven hills of wisdom, Mrs Root. Romulus and Remus, was it? Whelping in the streets. *Et tu, Brute*? We'll overnight here and merge in the morning.'

We check in at the Hotel Inghilterra where, in spite of the reassuring name, I have little confidence in the alarm call I book for half past eight and, as a consequence, I lie awake all night. At half past eight, I ring the porter. I give *him* an alarm call, in return stand still for a volley of Italian insolence.

All roads lead to Rome, but the celebrated Spanish Steps offer a handy place to take the weight off one's feet. My new shoes, modelled after the Mayor of Bologna's, have begun to pinch, but you must suffer to be *à la mode*.

Monday, 1st July 1991

A bowl of roughage, after which we take to the boulevards, myself fashionably attired in panama hat and shoes from Bologna, Mrs Root a shade less *à la mode*. As we stroll, I recce the shops in search of further accessories, while Mrs Root basks in the so-called beauty of the place. We reach the Spanish Steps, which I judge a handy place to take a breather.

'We'll sit down, Mrs Root. Take the weight off the feet.'

'It's all so beautiful, Henry. I really think I'd like to live here.'

'Do *what*, woman?' I can scarcely believe my ears.

'I mean I'd really like to stay here for a bit. There's so much to see. Couldn't we keep walking?'

I judge that I'd better knock this on the head as quickly and comfortably as possible.

'We'll not walk, Mrs Root, but if you're hell-bent on art we'll see it from the back of a charabanc. We'll do a tour. Art from the back of a bus. American Express will do something along these lines, I take it.'

As luck would have it, we find a travel agency not a stone's throw from the Spanish Steps. I approach the counter while Mrs Root leafs through tourist literature. I purchase two bus tickets for the tour of Ancient Rome, check the duration with the assistant.

'Two hours, *signore*.'

'As long as that, eh? Well, if you've nothing shorter.' I'm about to leave when I'm struck by a thought. 'Do you have a brochure on the Mafia, by the way?'

The assistant seems to take this as a wry comment of some sort, I don't know why. He turns away without replying, examines his papers with a tight expression. I address myself to Mrs Root.

'That didn't go down too well. Only recently made his bones, I dare say. The vow of silence. The canary that sang. Don't tell me.'

'Excuse me, *signore*,' the assistant says, 'but here in Italy the Mafia is hardly a laughing matter.'

I may have put my foot in it – not my way as a rule, but I'll own up to matters when I'm in the wrong.

'You misunderstand me, young man. I happen to be a serious investigator, covering all aspects of Italy for the BBC. You'd agree, I take it, that organised crime should be on the agenda?'

The assistant's demeanour changes immediately. "The BBC, *signore*? I apologise. But the Mafia is a sensitive subject. People do not like to talk about it – you never know who may be listening. A lot of people are under their control.'

'I see. Well – who can I speak to? Who can be trusted?'

The assistant shrugs. 'You could try to arrange a meeting with Leoluca Orlando, I suppose. But I doubt if you'd be successful.'

'Orlando, eh? I think he'd see me, young man. Who is he, by the way?'

'An outstanding man, *signore*.' The assistant speaks with undisguised admiration, his eyes are shining. 'In 1985 he was elected Mayor of Palermo. He brought 900 Mafia men to court in what became known as the Maxi-trials. He has now formed his own party, La Rete, which has sworn to rid Italy of corruption. He is a man of outstanding courage. There have been many threats against his life.'

I'm impressed. I like the sound of this chap Orlando. I straighten my shoulders.

'He's the man for me,' I say.

'I wish you luck, *signore*. Is there anything else?'

'Yes. Where did you get your suit?'

With the name of his outfitter on a card, we leave, shortly finding the departure point for our cultural tour. I raise my hat to a couple standing by the bus.

'Pardon me,' I say. 'Is this the queue for the Ancient Rome Express?'

'I certainly hope so,' the man says.

'Americans, Mrs Root. It will be wasted on them.' I turn to the couple. 'Just arrived, have you?'

'Yesterday,' the wife says. 'And tomorrow we're off to Venice.'

The info alerts Mrs Root, I'm sorry to say.

'Ooh Venice, Henry!' she says. 'I'd really like to see Venice. They say it's ever so romantic. We could go on a gondola.'

I jump on this one quickly. 'Like punting through a sewer, Mrs Root.' I address my American friends. 'You don't want to bother with

Known as the Yarmouth of the South, Venice became fashionable, briefly, as the haunt of aged homosexuals after Sir Dirk Bogarde starred there in *Death in Venice*. It is now admired chiefly as the location for the excellent Cornetti commercials. Coincidentally, Sir Dirk Bogarde is the most popular English filmstar in Italy after Barbara Windsor.

Venice. Did you know that a Doberman Pinscher, dropped in the Grand Canal, has a life expectancy of exactly three and a half seconds?'

The wife looks shocked. 'I don't like the sound of that, Hiram,' she says.

I press home my advantage. 'Well that's Venice, I'm afraid. Sinking into the sewers under the weight of its own corruption.'

'I tell you what, Ethel,' Hiram says. 'We'll give Venice a miss, I think. Thank you for the warning, sir.'

'Glad I was here to tip you off, Hiram,' I say. 'Mind you, there could be business opportunities there for myself and Branson. With a wrecking-ball and two days at our disposal we could flatten it and replace it with an Aqua Theme Park franchised to ourselves by Walt Disney Productions of the USA.'

I have Hiram's full attention now. 'You're in real estate?'

'Among other interests. At the moment I'm touring Europe on behalf of the BBC.'

Hiram's impressed. 'It's an honour to meet you, sir. Hiram and Ethel Schumacker from Ohio. Glad to make your acquaintance.'

'Henry and Muriel Root, Esher. How do you do?'

It's time to board the bus. I sit with my new American friends towards the back, while Mrs Root protests that she would have preferred to sit at the front, next to the tour guide – a dapper little Roman, who introduces himself as Roberto.

The Eternal City. At Mrs Root's insistence, we take in the sights from the back of an air-conditioned charabanc. Happily, a resourceful local operator lays on art for those in a hurry. I don't know much about Rome, but I know what I like.

'I'd like to hear the commentary,' she says.

'Never mind the commentary, Mrs Root,' I say. 'I'll be able to acquaint Hiram and Ethel here with anything appertaining.'

The bus sets off and I find myself competing with Roberto, who has the advantage of a PA system.

Driving past something called the Circus Maximus, he tells us that it's the largest ruin in the world, that it once seated 300,000 people. It's where the chariot races were held, he says.

That jogs the memory. I tap Hiram on the shoulder. 'I saw that one,' I say. '*Ben Hur*, wasn't it? Loved *him*, hated *her*! Oh dear oh dear!'

Hiram and Ethel rock with laughter at my little joke. Roberto seems displeased. He'll not be accustomed to having his thunder stolen.

'Don't mind me, Roberto! Just my little joke.'

I return to my theme. 'Burt Lancaster, wasn't it? Or was it the stiff one? The one with the head? Charlton Heskith?'

'Heston,' says Ethel.

'Thank you, Ethel.'

'I prefer Kirk Douglas, myself,' Ethel says. 'I've always liked Kirk Douglas.'

'I know the one you mean,' I say. '*Spartacus*, wasn't it? Kirk Douglas is only four foot nine, you know. When he played opposite Jean Simmons in *Spartacus* she was obliged to partake of her love scenes standing in a hole.'

Another American lady now gets up and joins Hiram, Ethel and myself at the back of the bus.

'Blanche Beauregarde from Alabama,' she says. 'I've always admired Jean Simmons. She was my favourite. Whatever became of Jean Simmons, I wonder?'

An American, dressed in tartan shorts, leans forward, taps me on the shoulder.

'I like Glenn Ford,' he says. 'I never miss a Glenn Ford picture.'

One prefers, of course, not to disabuse a fan, but I feel I have to put him right.

'You surprise me, frankly. Never been able to see the point of Glenn Ford myself. Neither one thing nor the other, if you have my drift.'

'Glenn Ford,' says my friend in tartan shorts, 'was a real-life war hero.'

'Is that so? Well, perhaps that was the point of him. Up a hill. "Follow me, men!" Blown to bits. *The Red Badge Of Courage*.'

At this point our driver narrowly avoids collison with a mad Italian in a Fiat, occasioning a squeal of brakes and a volley on both sides of scorching imprecations.

'Mad as hatters,' I explain. 'Like children. I've heard it said that in Naples the bus conductors get a bonus each month if they refrain from hitting the passengers. No manners, do you see? A faulty sense of *comme il faut*. Hence your – er – I'll not say the word in front of Roberto here. Lips sealed and so forth. Don't want to land head first in the Tiber in a concrete waistcoat.'

I hum a few bars of the *Godfather* theme, have difficulty against Roberto's insistent flow of historical info in conveying my musical gist. Roberto burbles on, mentions a magnificent awning, operated by a corps of sailors, which provided shade for the spectators.

'I've got it!' Hiram cries. '*The Godfather*! Mr Root's talking about the Mafia.'

'Precisely, Hiram – though I'd be obliged if you'd keep your voice down. They're all in it, do you see? I read recently that at Naples Central Criminal Court last year, twenty-seven men faced charges of extortion, murder, arson, assault, bombing and slander. The defendants were nine monks, seven schoolteachers, five doctors, three policemen and the Mayor. All were acquitted. The Chief Prosecutor lodged an appeal but before this could be heard he was arrested for running a brothel.'

My audience's eyes are out like organ-stops.

'It is probable,' Roberto says, 'that the Colosseum would still be standing today were it not for violent earthquakes of the thirteenth and fourteenth centuries. . . .'

'Never mind that, Roberto,' I say. 'Oh yes, Ethel. Shocking business. Young man, nice suit, hair parted in the middle, kisses Momma goodbye in the morning, goes out and shoots three men in a barber's shop. Then it's home to Momma and the meatballs.'

Roberto announces that it's now time to leave the bus. We have reached the Forum, he says, which can best be approached on foot. Arrived at the Forum, Roberto proudly informs us that our law is essentially based on Roman law.

'Don't tell me, Roberto,' I say. 'Crassus the law-maker. And the other one. Cicero, was it? Plus Seneca, the old cynic. Rolled round Rome in a barrel looking for an honest man. Not surprised he didn't find one – in the wrong neck of the woods entirely! Don't mind me, Roberto! Just my little joke.'

'The ruins as we see them today,' says Roberto, 'are essentially those of the Forum as modified in the reign of . . .'

'The Ides of March,' I say. '"Yon Cassius has a lean and hungry look." Marlo Brandon?'

'I do like him,' says Eleanor from Philadelphia.

'You'd be better off with Gregory Peck, madam,' I say. 'Marlo Brandon has recently ballooned up to twenty-five stone. Like Elvis Presley. Isn't that right, Ethel?'

Before Ethel can answer, a fourth American lady, not previously of my group, instructs Roberto to hold his horses for the moment, thereafter joining up with us.

The famous Colosseum (*left*). To the casual observer, it looks as if Liverpool were playing here last week. In fact, it's where the ancient Romans – ever ones to fix a fight – matched a hundred ecstatic Christians against a solitary lion. Similarly, your contemporary Italian has little sense of what is and isn't cricket. When an Italian crew won the European coxless fours on Lake Como in 1987, they were steered from the bows by a Sicilian dwarf.

'I like Elvis Presley,' she says. 'He's still alive, you know. There have been many sightings. He was last seen at the first night of *Aspects of Love* in New York.'

'Nonsense, madam,' I say. It's not like me to be dogmatic, but I feel I have to put her right. 'Elvis Presley spent the last two years of his life in a fur-lined room, existing on a diet of hamburgers and fizzy drinks. When he died he was too fat to be slotted through the door of his bedroom and had to be winched to the waiting hearse at the end of a crane.'

We're almost at the end of the tour, thank goodness, have now arrived at the so-called Trevi Fountain, where Roberto explains that if you throw a coin into the water it means you'll return to Rome one day. It seems only fair to put him right on that.

'We'll not want to do that, thank you very much, Roberto. No offence meant. Enough's enough and so forth.' I advise my party to keep their money in their purses. '*La Dolce Vita*, was it? The big Swede in the fountain? On all fours in her dinner dress? You'll remember it, Ethel.'

'Anita Ekberg,' Ethel says.

'That's the one. I wonder what became of her? Oh well. They come and they go. The moon's a balloon. Done much shopping, have you, Ethel? They've got some very nice shops – I'll say that for them.'

Mention of shopping reminds me that I wish to purchase a suit fashioned in the style of the one worn by the assistant at the travel agency. I decide that the conducted tour is over, announce my decision to my party. My American friends gather round, pump my

Some are born great, some have greatness thrust upon them. I've taken over from Roberto, the dapper little tour guide. It takes an Englishman to point out the special peculiarities of the passing show.

hand, thank me for a most instructive afternoon. Roberto, seeing that his job is done, asks if anyone has a final question.

'Just one, Roberto,' I say. 'Where did you get your handbag?'

Tuesday, 2nd July 1991

I've not been idle *in re* my reconnaissance for Hussey, Lord Weidenfeld of Nicolson and the BBC. I've purchased a sharp Italian suit after the manner of the one worn by the travel agent, plus a handbag like Roberto's. Both accoutrements, I think, look better on me.

The tour over, I pose for Ethel's camera against a ruin. In fashion-conscious Italy, men account for eighty-two per cent of the readership of *Vogue* and *Harpers & Queen*. There's little doubt that I look the part and I read nothing but the *Telegraph*.

And, as importantly, I've arranged a rendezvous – using a scrambled line (I utilise a phone *kiosko*, to be precise) – with Leoluca Orlando, the little Mayor of Palermo, as was. I emerge from the *kiosko*, having rung his political HQ, instruct Mrs Root to ready the video equipment. I glance cautiously to left and right.

'Confidential audio-visual *aide-mémoire* for Hussey. "The Root Report on Europe". Entry Five.' I continue in a low, top-security whisper. 'Somewhere in Rome. For my ears only. I've been in contact with the headquarters of La Rete. A rendezvous has been arranged. Myself and Orlando, the little Mafia hunter. The venue at his country retreat, south of Rome. We depart immediately under plain cover. Should anything happen to me this tape must be destroyed. Over and out.'

I can't help noticing that quite a crowd has gathered. Old men exchange confidential nods and mutterings. It occurs to me that I may have given away Orlando's hitherto top-secret whereabouts. Not my fault. Rushes for Hussey are of the essence.

We drive south out of Rome, head towards Naples, deep into Mafia territory. We reach a little village, come upon a roadside *trattoria*, where I decide we'll stop for lunch. Aware that we may be being followed, I park discreetly behind a tree. We stroll casually into the *trattoria*'s courtyard where a large, festive family lunch is already in progress. We sit at an empty table, are ignored entirely for the moment.

'Perhaps they're not open to the public,' Mrs Root observes.

'Quite possibly not, Mrs Root,' I say. 'However, we can't leave now. We have in all likelihood wandered into the lion's den. We don't want to draw attention to ourselves.'

'If we don't draw attention to ourselves, Henry, how are we going to get anything to eat?'

I've sussed things out, explain our highly dangerous circumstances to Mrs Root.

'All in good time, Mrs Root. We've stumbled into it, do you see? A board meeting's in progress, involving the entire family. The fat one in braces, he'll be the Don. We'll not instruct him to bring us the menu. The two younger men over there – they'll be *capo di tuttis*. The old woman ladling out the stew – she'll be Momma. Keep absolutely still – as we did in Essential Spain when confronted by the bull. Oh oh – too late, they've spotted us. Don't mention cement.'

On the way south for our secret rendezvous with Leoluca Orlando, the little Mafia hunter, we stumble by mistake into a 'family' meeting. The Don, with arms crossed, is flanked by Momma, who has taken time off from stirring meatballs in the kitchen, and by the local priest. My guess is the priest will be on bail for bombing and extortion.

The Don himself has left the party and is walking towards our table.

'Oh my good God. The Don wants a word. Act natural.'

The Don smiles cheerfully – he'll not fool me, he'd smile like this before putting his own *consigliere* in the freezer – asks us in Italian what we'd like to eat. He then embarks upon an all-too-telling mime, placing four stubby fingers against his lips – *Omerta*, the vow of silence!

I quickly reassure him. 'Point taken, Don. I have you. *Omerta*. The canary that sang. Nod's as good as a wink.'

I'm obliged to sample Momma's cooking. If they suspected my links with Orlando, it would be the French kiss and the concrete overcoat. I'd be feeding the fishes.

Mrs Root, by a lucky chance, then leaps to the right conclusion, twigs that this is a double bluff, a message within a message, that the Don is using the *Omerta* mime to ask us what we want to eat. I keep my counsel, allow her to order pasta and a bottle of *vino tinto*.

'Well done, woman,' I say. 'He's got me down as an idiot. All part of my plan.'

Our food arrives, a man in fancy dress appears with an accordion, the younger family members start an energetic dance. There is laughter and flirtatiousness, the Don and Momma join the tarantella, everyone claps and cheers. Mrs Root drops her guard, seems to enjoy this threadbare charade, so I tip her off.

'There are those who could be fooled by this, Mrs Root. Looks innocent enough. A few peasants kicking up their heels. A family knees-up. Nothing wrong with that, the uninitiated might suppose. We know better. One word out of place and we'd be head first into a bollard. We'd be feeding the fishes in a concrete overcoat.'

Mrs Root still seems unaware of our perilous situation.

'Surely not, Henry,' she says. 'They all look ever so nice.'

'Nice, Mrs Root?!? If they – oh oh, here comes trouble.'

The Don has taken one of the younger men in a bear-like hug.

'There you are, Mrs Root. If he kisses him on the mouth he's a dead duck. Full on the lips, tongue down the throat like a Dynarod – means you've had it. Into the freezer, upside down on a meat hook. We've seen too much.'

There's worse to come. A young couple, laughing merrily, dance past our table, pull us to our feet.

'Act naturally, Mrs Root. Pretend to enjoy yourself.'

We become caught up in the happy whirl, we're passed around like

We maintain our cover by doing the tarantella with the 'family'. A little *capo di tutti capi* has Mrs Root in a half nelson, while the *consiglieri*'s sister makes me an offer I can't refuse. It's a ladies' 'excuse me', I think.

parcels in a musical game. When the music stops we drop giddily into the nearest seats.

'That was invigorating, Henry,' says Mrs Root.

'We're lucky to be alive, Mrs Root. Let's not press our luck further. We'll be off now.'

I ask for the bill, but to my dismay the Don refuses to accept my money. He's trying to compromise me, to put me in his debt. If I don't pay, he'll pitch up in Esher for a favour. He'll make me an offer I can't refuse. It's no good. After a minute or so of financial push and pull I concede as gracefully as I can. We are embraced by the family, who then gather to see us off. Once in the safety of the car, I congratulate myself on the way I handled a dangerous situation.

'I don't normally blow my bags, Mrs Root, but I handled that pretty well, I think. If they'd suspected my links with Orlando – oh dear oh dear . . . we'd not be here to tell the tale.'

I start the engine, whereupon the car backfires dramatically. The whole family – Don, Momma, *capo di tuttis* – dive for safety underneath a table.

'*Mafiosi!*' says the Don, tapping the side of his nose.

I drive away as fast as I can.

'We were lucky, Mrs Root. They took me for a made man. A man of respect such as themselves. It was touch and go.'

We drive south, towards Naples, for my rendezvous with Leoluca Orlando, the little Mafia hunter. I am unable, of course, to divulge the exact locale – sufficient to say it is not a million miles away from a Holiday Inn on the outskirts of Naples.

I deposit Mrs Root in the Executive Lounge, announce my mission at the desk, am escorted by bodyguards to an upstairs suite. I'm frisked outside the door, am then allowed to enter. Orlando – a dark,

When in Rome . . . At Orlando's secret hideaway, I'm frisked in the vestibule by two of his bodyguards – an experience I'd not undergone before. Anyone frisking me in Esher would go headfirst into a municipal rubbish tip.

not unimpressive-looking little man – is sitting at a table, with a bodyguard on either side. He gets up to greet me.

'Good of you to see me, *Señor* Orlando,' I say. 'Henry Root. Special Constable. A man of action like yourself. Peas in a pod, in fact.'

Orlando looks at me somewhat warily. You can't blame him, I suppose. He'll not have had time to make a judgement.

'Is that so?' he says. 'Well – how can I help you?'

I start with a little deep background *in re* myself.

'I'm the British PM's Man without Portfolio,' I say. 'I have, too, worked closely with Sir Mark, as was, and Sir Anderton, God's Copper. Plus and further, I'm known to Captain Paulus of Paris's Fifth Arrondissement. I'm currently investigating all aspects of Italy for the BBC. Can't avoid mentioning the Mafia. Small subject, I dare say, an exaggerated problem no doubt – popularised by Hollywood and so forth – but I'll have to touch on it. Got it under control, have you? A few fat men in braces, is that the size of it? On top of it, are you?'

Mr Orlando surprises me somewhat with his response. He becomes quite heated, gesticulates and at one point thumps the table. He suggests that I have quite misunderstood the nature of the problem, that no one, least of all the police, is on top of it.

'It is typically English,' he says, 'to regard the Mafia as some tropical disease which cannot be caught by more civilised countries. In fact it is a cancer deep within Italy's very bowels. Nor is it a problem which the police can solve. It isn't a fight between the Mafia and the State, Mr Root, it is a fight between different factions within the State. One side fights the Mafia, the other protects it – by appointing corrupt judges, magistrates and so forth. The solution must be political, which is why I have formed my own party, La Rete.'

'Well done,' I say. 'Strength to your elbow, Mr Orlando. However, here's my gist. If what you say is true – if the Mafia is such an enormous threat – will not 1992, the lowering of barriers, the dismantling of frontiers etc., represent some danger to the rest of Europe? That's my concern. It's on that point that I wish to report back to the British PM, Hussey and Lord Weidenfeld of Nicolson.'

'You mean, can the tropical disease spread to more advanced civilisations?'

'My point precisely. With frontiers opening up, might not men of respect carry their violin cases hither and thither throughout the Community? We'll not want Godfathers in the British High Street, thank you very much, shotguns in Sainsbury's, Momma cooking meatballs at the bingo club.'

Mr Orlando, I'm glad to say, is able to reassure me. 'I don't think you'd need worry about that, Mr Root. Nothing will change.'

'I'm relieved to hear you say that, Leoluca. The Mafia, I'm sure, would get short shrift outside Italy.'

'Wrong again, Mr Root. The situation won't change for the simple reason that the Mafia is already well established in Europe.'

I'll not let him get away with that. 'Now look here, Leoluca, don't tell me. . . .'

'No, Mr Root – *you look here*. Consider this. A burglar notices that one house has an expensive new burglar alarm and another house has no alarm. Which will he break into? I use this analogy to explain why the Mafia has spread already into the rest of Europe. These countries have been slow to install an alarm system. Nor are the Mafia baggy-trousered moustachioed Dons, but educated men in suits – lawyers, accountants, bankers and politicians. It is not the Sicilian Dons who

In the course of our top-level discussions, Orlando broods on the fact that in some parts of southern Italy seventy-one per cent of the male population are employed full-time either by the police or by the Mafia, and of these, forty-eight per cent are believed to be employed by both.

are in Europe, but the politicians who represent them. The Mafia are in Brussels, Mr Root.'

I'm shaken slightly, I must admit. 'This is disturbing, Leoluca, I grant you that. Indeed, I'll tip off my man in Brussels, Bill Martin. However, England isn't France or Spain, still less Italy. Our burglar alarms are of the best. I refer to Scotland Yard.'

I had him there, I'll wager. I'd confounded him this time.

'In fact,' says Orlando, 'Scotland Yard was particularly slow to react to the Mafia threat – with the result that the Mafia now control organised crime in London. Let me tell you this. In the early seventies, Leggio Luciano – boss of the Corleone Family in Sicily – sent the Caruana brothers and Francesco di Carlo to London to organise the distribution of hard drugs. Soon after this, Ninni Cassara, Palermo's top detective, went to London to inform Scotland Yard of the dangers. They laughed at him. A senior officer in the Narcotics Control and Intelligence Unit said "We have no Mafia problem here in London." Cassara returned to Palermo in despair at the ignorance of the British, and a few days later he was murdered by the Mafia. Di Carlo has since been arrested and convicted, but at least sixty top Mafia men have taken his place in the United Kingdom.'

I'm not in the least confounded. I'm dealing here with an excitable Southern European type, prone to exaggeration.

'You'll excuse me, Leoluca, if I take what you say with a pinch of salt. I have one slight advantage over you, you see. I happen to be English, I live in England. I think I'd have noticed if olive-skinned young men were lounging around Esher High Street with their violin cases at the ready. Still – you'll lead an exciting life, I imagine, and if you ever want a safe house in Esher mine will be at your disposal. Myself standing shotgun on the porch, Mrs Root stirring meatballs in the kitchen. . . .'

To my amazement, Orlando suddenly explodes. 'This isn't a game, Mr Root!' he shouts. He bangs the table. 'You haven't understood a word I've said! You are the stupidest man I've ever met . . . !'

I'm not sitting still for this. He's taken leave of his senses. I stand up, move with dignity towards the door.

'I am at risk from you!' Orlando shouts. 'From your ignorance and stupidity. My enemies are threefold: the Dons in Sicily who control everything with violence and money. The men in suits – the politicians, the lawyers and bankers – who allow themselves to be bought, who buy shares in Mafia controlled companies and follow their rise and fall in the *Wall Street Journal* and the *Daily Telegraph*. And people like you who, through ignorance or apathy, allow the cancer to spread. You are a puppet, Mr Root!'

I'm practically speechless – I've not been called that before – but I find my voice. 'Do what!?! A puppet? I'll thank you . . .'

'No – I'll thank *you*, Mr Root. Your strings are controlled by your idiotic preconceptions, by your attendance at a hundred third-rate Hollywood films. The Mafia should give you a prize for your co-operation.'

I think this excitable little Italian has finally run out of steam, but he suddenly rounds on his bodyguards.

'Leave the room!' he shouts. 'You can't help me here. You can protect me from an assassin's bullet, but not from blind ignorance. You are the danger, Mr Root! You're a puppet!'

I've heard enough. I turn on my heel and leave the room, return to the lobby and gather Mrs Root.

'What was he like, Henry?' she asks.

'Rudest man I ever met, Mrs Root. And now I'm compromised, I wouldn't wonder. In a barber's shop having a shave one day, three men come through the door with tommy-guns, over I go in a blaze of bullets. *Stupid* man!'

I pull my hat over my eyes, instruct Mrs Root to leave the lobby first – a decoy or sitting duck, as it were – follow her at a secure distance, having informed a functionary in the vestibule that there's a man in the corner of the lounge reading the *Daily Telegraph*.

'He'll be one of them,' I say. 'A Mafia puppet, do you see? Checking his stocks and shares.'

Out in the street, I walk ten yards astern of Mrs Root – eyes scanning in a wide arc like a radar beam – catch sight of an *à la mode* overcoat in a gentleman's boutique, enter and purchase it. I recover my customary *sang froid*, but continue to use Mrs Root as sitting duck until we reach the car.

Wednesday, 3rd July 1991

Here's an oddity. I'm quite enjoying Italy, am beginning to feel at home. In my new wardrobe I increasingly blend with the local populace, have picked up the strutting walk plus a range of oaths and gesticulations with which I can communicate. I'm sitting now at what was once Mrs Root's dressing-table, confronted by my collection of newly acquired gentlemen's toiletries – lined up in place of the Carmen curlers. I pluck a nasal hair, apply a dab of Armani's Jungle Glade behind the ear.

'You're taking your time, Henry,' says Mrs Root.

How typical of a woman to chivvy one during one's toilet preparations.

'Important rendezvous this morning, Mrs Root. Madame Cicciolina, no less. The dancing MP and and Page Three girl. We're meeting at her club. The Blue Moon. She's a *chanteuse*, do you see? The protest songs, I wouldn't wonder. Stuff with a political slant, she'll touch on the environment, I'd guess. You'll be all right, will you?'

'I'll be fine, Henry,' she says. 'I'll be working too. I'm meeting the wife of a Euro-MP.'

I'm startled, I must say, suspend my cosmetic operations for the moment.

Prior to my rendez-vous with Madame Cicciolina, the little Italian vaudeville *artiste*, I put the finishing touches to my cosmetic preparations. Appearance isn't everything, but, as Anna Raeburn has correctly said, to respect others you must first respect yourself.

'Oh yes? And who might she be?'

'Marina Ripa de Meana, Henry. She's at the centre of the in-crowd. An expert on everything – style, fashion, she's written two autobiographies full of the most intimate details about her personal life. It's the *Dolce Vita* really.'

I suppress a chuckle, it's not my way to leave someone feeling like a pricked balloon. This is a laugh, however. If anyone is to investigate the *Dolce Vita* it should be me, of course. Mrs Root has neither the wardrobe nor the small talk, the necessary badinage.

'The *Dolce Vita*, Mrs Root? Not really you, is it? What time's this then?'

'This afternoon,' she says. 'We're meeting at a new art gallery that she's opening. I'll really enjoy that. Then she's going to show me over her fashion house.'

I'm uncharacteristically put out. Natural protectiveness, I suppose. I like to know where Mrs Root is, that she's sticking to the prepared agenda.

'Where will I meet you, then?'

'Well, you could meet us for tea, I suppose. She always has tea at Babington's near the Spanish Steps. But you wouldn't be interested in seeing her fashion house. That's not your thing, is it? Fashion?'

This time I can't suppress a chuckle.

'Oh dear oh dear. On the contrary, Mrs Root, I like to keep an eye on what's currently *à la mode*. I'll meet you at this Babington's place. Four-thirty, say?'

I arrive at the Blue Moon Club by cab and saunter inside – distancing myself from the other punters in the foyer by the way I carry off my expensive wardrobe, by my casual, take-me-or-leave-me manner. I am carrying a bunch of red roses for Madame Cicciolina. I am a little early, decide, on a whim, to see the show before our rendezvous.

I enter the auditorium, dislodge a punter from a front-row centre seat ('Excuse me, personal friend, do you see') and settle down just as the compère announces the star of the show, Ilona Stalla, 'La Cicciolina'.

I applaud with gusto – my hands freezing in mid-air as I notice that this Cicciolina creature is stone naked back and front. I slump poleaxed in my seat, hide my face behind the roses, address the punter I dislodged.

It's not generally known that actors in Italy only got the vote in 1967. This picture of Madame Cicciolina explains why, perhaps.

'My mistake,' I say. 'Hardly know the woman – don't know her at all, in fact.'

I make my escape, run for the foyer, where I'm fielded by a member of the management.

'Mr Root?' he says.

'No,' I say.

He doesn't seem to understand, marches me briskly backstage, and deposits me in the little nudist's dressing-room. She is wearing a fur coat and, all too obviously, nothing underneath. It's not like me to be confounded but I find I've lost the power of speech. I have also lost the ability to coordinate my movements. I attempt to hand the roses to this Cicciolina creature, realise that I can't do this while searching for my business card, therefore hand the roses to the member of the management and hand my card to Cicciolina. Then, realising my mistake, I recover the roses from the management, hand them to Cicciolina, give the card to the management and then take back the roses.

Such is the effect on an Englishman when confronted at close quarters with pornography. Let no one sneer at Mary Kenny or my friend Lord Longford.

The creature speaks. 'So, Mr Root. How can,I help you?'

She'd better not try, I think. I put myself on full alert. I open and shut my mouth.

'You liked the show?' she says.

I find at last that I can speak. 'Er – first class, madam. What I saw of it. Not a theatrical myself, more of a naval man. Seen the world. The red light up an alley. Port Said, was it? The bump and grind behind a curtain. Takes a bit to shock me. I expect you know what you're doing. What are you doing?'

'Enjoying myself, Mr Root,' the creature says. 'Or can I call you Henry? I'm an entertainer. I like to make people happy.'

'An entertainer, eh? Politics and showbiz – is that the mix? It's been done before, I grant you. Reagan. He was one. The Redgrave woman – she was another. Isadora Duncan, was it? Dancing at midnight on her lover's lawn adorned in a serviette. Plus Dame Jackson. She didn't take her clothes off, I'm glad to say. Yes she did. Oh dear oh dear. I'd say this, however. On being elected to office, none of the aforesaid continued to dance in public, still less without their clothes. Why do you still do it, madam?'

I've got the woman here. I've clapped her in a paradox. I've recovered my confidence. I take a sip of the Champagne proffered. I begin to feel quite cheerful.

'It's a political gesture, Henry,' the woman says.

She's not such a bad old tart, I suddenly conclude. She'd better not try it on with, that's all. Her fur coat falls open, revealing an expanse of soft, buttery thigh. I'm unaffected. I'm an Englishman.

'I want to shock people,' she says. 'I want to make them realise that there are worse things than a display of public nudity.'

'With respect, madam,' I say, 'it's hard to imagine what. The return of a Labour government, perhaps. Her Majesty abdicating in favour of Raine Spenser. The big lad Gooch bowled first ball by a little Calypso Cavalier. Class war anarchists throwing lobsters at their betters in the Pimms tent at Henley Regatta. Alternative comedians in place of Sir Secombe's *Highway*.'

Tête à tête in the hot minx's dressing-room. She'd better not attempt the funny stuff with me. I'm a married man from England's green belt. That said, you can't blame her for finding me attractive, I suppose.

I've silenced the woman, I imagine, but she continues unabashed.

'Frankly, Henry,' she says, 'I was referring to man's inhumanity to man – war, famine, pollution, cruelty.'

She's walked into my trap. As I suspected, she's a woolly-minded environmental buff.

'Bit outdated that sort of stuff, isn't it? Smacks of the sixties to me. Do your thing. Let it all hang out. Peace through nudity. *Hair*, was it? The Princess Royal jack naked on the stage? Plus the Isle of Wight. The little American crooner with a banjo and a flower up his nose? Bob Dylan? The Poet of the Open Road? A blowin' in the wind? Don't tell me.'

The woman won't be silenced. 'But what was wrong with the sixties, Henry? Young people enjoying themselves. All quite harmless. They were expressing themselves, revealing their emotions in public. Very healthy, I'd have thought.'

Oh dear oh dear. We've heard all this before. I have to correct her. 'Such behaviour is unseemly, madam. A person's emotions should stay corsetted, elsewise where would we all be?'

'You're getting quite hot under the collar, Henry!'

The woman laughs, allows her coat to fall open still more revealingly. I begin to think she finds me fatally attractive. I decide to hit this one firmly on the head.

'An Englishman, madam, never gets hot under anything.'

The woman can't be staunched. I'll have to inform the minx that I'm a married man, else I fear she might get me in a headlock, wrap her soft white velvety thighs . . . oh my good God. She moves towards me.

'What are you so afraid of, Henry? The sex drive is a beautiful thing. A gift from God. I believe we're here to enjoy ourselves.'

I've heard enough. I get up, move towards the door, keeping her within my sights.

'That's as may be, madam – although it isn't. I'll say this, however. Er – I'll be off now.'

I'm halfway to safety when the esurient harpie seeks to detain me.

'Do *you* enjoy yourself, Henry?'

'Of course I do, woman! Good heavens – I . . . I . . .'

'Well you should enjoy yourself. An attractive man like you. You should be having the time of your life. Relax! Loosen up! Throw off your English inhibitions! You think about what I've said.'

I make my escape, walk back towards the auditorium. My brain's in a turmoil, reeling with unaccustomed notions. Should people enjoy themselves? That can't be right. Where would we be if everyone enjoyed themselves? Sodom and Gomorrah, that's where. The woman's dangerous. I shake my head vigorously, as if to dislodge water from the auditory canals and find myself walking across the stage – 'Excuse me, madam, I was unaware there was a show in progress' – and reach the auditorium. I'm about to enter the foyer when I change my mind. I return to the auditorium and slip into an empty seat. No harm in seeing the show again. Just to confirm my thinking.

I'll confess this: the next hour or two is something of a blank. It can be thus with those of us who have outstanding powers of concentration. They say that when Gary Player, the little South African golfer, was head down over a vital putt, Concorde could have passed overhead and he wouldn't have been aware of it. It is the same with me when I'm beset with a conundrum or large idea. I must somehow have left the Blue Moon Theatre and found my way to Babington's Tea

Rooms, but so deeply was I concentrating on this new and heavy notion that I don't know how.

Should people enjoy themselves? More specifically, should I enjoy myself? By which I mean *enjoy* myself – as per the volatile little Italians to left and right. The question buzzed in my head like a wasp in a jamjar. Prior to this I'd have said, if asked, that of course I enjoy myself – in a normal way. Up in the morning. Breakfast, the *Daily Telegraph*, a glance at the crossword. 'Good morning Mrs Root. Funny sort of day. Neither one thing nor the other.' A stroll on my front lawn. Into my study to deal with the correspondence, to juggle my endowment policies and index-linked pension schemes. A sherry wine before lunch, perhaps. *Mavis at One*. In the afternoon, a brisk walk, unaccompanied, through Esher's leafy avenues. Tea. The BBC Six O'clock News rendered by Anna Ford for preference. A sherry wine. Dinner. Haddock-in-the-bag if the choice has been mine, followed by Findus's Cherry Trifle in a carton. After dinner, feet up in front of the television. *Ask Anneka. That's Life*. Bed.

Enjoyable of course, but not, I think, what Madame Cicciolina had in mind.

'You're an attractive man, Henry,' she'd said. 'You should do your thing.'

I've never done that, I've never done my thing, either in Esher or elsewhere. And this is the question now buzzing in my brain, which is

I've survived my meeting with Madame Cicciolina. Still carrying the floral tribute meant for her – I don't know why – I pace the Via Veneto in the grip of a large conundrum. Should one let it all hang out, as advised by Madame Cicciolina? I'm off now to meet Mrs Root – not what the minx had in mind, perhaps. . . .

still insistently buzzing there when I pitch up at Babington's for my meeting with Mrs Root and her contact, the Ripa de Meana woman.

Should I do my thing?

Mrs Root is greeting me, I think, but I scarcely hear her, any more than Gary Player, the little golfer, can hear Concorde passing overhead.

'What's that, Mrs Root?' I say.

'You're covered in lipstick, Henry,' she says.

'I dare say I am, Mrs Root,' I say.

'Here, let me dab it off. And you're eating my cucumber sandwich. Really – you're quite distracted, Henry. What's on your mind?'

At this moment the Ripa woman makes a dramatic entrance amid a swirl of attention. She's not unpleasing – in an overstated Italian way – and her arrival has the effect of releasing me somewhat from my reverie. I'm an attractive man, after all – designated thus by an Italian minx, I'll work my magic with this other one. I hold myself suavely, after the manner of a matinée sophisticate.

'You'll be Henry,' the Ripa woman says.

She holds out her hand, which I ignore. I kiss her lightly on both cheeks.

'*Enchanté*, I'm sure,' I say. 'I hope my wife hasn't been boring you.'

'On the contrary,' she says. 'We have become firm friends. This afternoon we visited a gallery together. Do you like art, Henry?'

I essay a sophisticated jest. 'Art who?' I say. 'No no – just my little joke, my dear. Art is one of my greatest interests. Picasso, was it? And the other one. Hockney? Herr Issyvoo by a pool. A well-formed youth knifing the azure water. Don't tell me.'

The Ripa woman is by no means unattractive. Not as attractive, though, as the Cicciolina creature. And that's odd. I hadn't succumbed to Cicciolina in her dressing-room. Quite the opposite. Still waters and so forth, I suppose. With a real man such as myself, feelings take time to surface. They don't burst into exotic life, flourish briefly for a day and then expire. I'd not been unaware of her soft, creamy thighs, of course, the dark mysterious secrets of her exposed . . . I feel a little breathless, I steady myself against a chair.

'Are you all right, Henry?' asks Mrs Root.

'Perfectly all right, thank you, Mrs Root,' I say.

'So – what gives, girls?' I take to the parlance like a duck to water. 'Where's it at?'

The Ripa woman looks at her watch. 'It's time to move on, I think. I'm taking Muriel to see my showroom.'

'Great,' I say. 'Good show. Let's rock around the clock.'

The Ripa woman and Mrs Root seem surprised that I wish to tag along. I'm cool. I know when to split. I hold up a hand to stem the invitation.

'You chicks carry on. I'll hang loose. Do my thing.'

Mrs Root shows unnecessary concern on my behalf. 'Will you be all right?' she says. 'We'll meet this evening then?'

'Whatever. See you later, alligator.'

I aim for the exit, walking with nonchalance from the waist. I head west, towards the Via Veneto – the celebrated haunt of cinema entrepreneurs and their young companions – pass an expensive optician's shop, in whose window I spot a pair of shades similar to those worn by Madame Cicciolina's manager. I enter and purchase them, later catch sight of myself in a window, am pleased to see that I look the part – an attractive *boulevardier* out on his evening stroll. I arrive at the café where I'm to rendezvous with Mrs Root, make a sophisticated entrance. I saunter inside, pose casually until fielded by a waiter.

'*Uno, signore?*'

Style wars. Confronting the rest of the fashion-conscious clientèle, I hold my own at a chic café, while waiting for Mrs Root. My new shades doubtless cost more than your trousers, honest reader, but it's the expression in the eyes behind the shades which spells Style with a capital S.

I give him a withering look from behind my shades. 'Do I look like an *uno*, Giuseppe? I shall be joined shortly by a lady.'

I'm placed at a table for two. Giuseppe hands me a menu, waits for my order. Again I have to put the fellow right.

'It is customary,' I say, 'not to hog oneself before the arrival of one's guest. Done this sort of job before, have you, Giuseppe?'

Giuseppe mutters something and retires. Two chic young girls at the next table have a fit of giggles. They have enjoyed the exchange between me and Giuseppe, I imagine. I smile at them and wink. They look away, are consumed again by a fit of giggles. I've scored a hit, there's little doubt of that. The Cicciolina woman knew what she was on about.

Two young men at a nearby table are having a heated argument. They raise their voices, poke each other in the chest. It's up to me – a Special Constable in Esher, an associate here of Orlando the little Mafia hunter – to intervene, to maintain law and order. I approach their table, say, 'Hey, cool it, you cats,' or something along those lines, am set back on my heels by a volley of Italian insults. I return to my table. I'd done my best – as would have been obvious to the two pretty lasses on my left. They are looking at me with open admiration, so I give them a flashing smile. They cover their mouths and shake with helpless laughter. I've certainly had a strange effect on them. Madame Cicciolina had been right.

Giuseppe appears suddenly at my shoulder, suggests again that I order something to eat. To keep the fellow quiet I ask for a beer. He looks displeased, I don't know why. I notice another single man across the room, rather admire the way he has undone his collar and loosened his tie. He looks relaxed and sure of himself. Giuseppe won't harass him at regular intervals, I'll wager. I loosen my collar and tie, then I remove my coat and place it on the spare chair. I decide to buy a drink for the two lasses on my left. I turn to speak to them, am slightly discommoded to discover that they've been joined at their table by the two conceited young Romans who, earlier – and but for my intervention – would have come to blows. The four of them look at me and start to laugh. It occurs to me that they may suppose I've been stood up. I'm tempted to look at my watch, but realise in time that to do so might suggest a lack of nonchalance. In my shades, its characters would not, in any case, be visible.

Giuseppe returns with my beer. An elegant woman in her early forties enters. I smile at her while pouring my beer and, thus distracted, pour a quantity of it into my lap. I mop myself down, place my coat over my legs to hide the stain. The café is now completely full. A man enters and joins the party of young people at the next table. He asks me if my spare chair is free, starts to carry it off. I spring upright to defend it, dropping my coat to reveal my beer-stained trousers. The young man retires, but his friends break into laughter once again – and at me this time, I think, not with me.

To Giuseppe's displeasure I click my fingers in his direction, order some nuts to go with my beer. The café is bursting at the seams, several customers have their eye on my empty chair. I begin to feel a little disconsolate, I must admit. I'm gripped by an emotion not previously experienced: I'd give up a franchise or two to see the reassuring sight of Mrs Root coming through the door. My trousers are wet, my new shoes from Bologna are starting to pinch. I take off my shades, catch sight of myself in a mirror. I look ridiculous. More accurately, like a four-square Englishman of mature years mimicking an Italian pimp. I've had enough. I get up to go, walk into Mrs Root coming through the door. I'm about to say something which later I might regret. I pull myself together in the nick of time, make her fully aware of my displeasure.

'What on earth kept you, woman? I was about to leave.'

Mrs Root grabs the stick by the wrong end, imagines that I'd been lost without her.

'I'm really sorry, Henry,' she says. 'I was enjoying myself so much I completely lost track of the time.' She gives me a curious look, suddenly breaks into an idiotic smile. 'I believe you missed me!'

'Don't be so silly, woman.'

I take her arm in a proprietorial grip, steer her towards the door, wink at the party of four.

'Women!' I say. I raise my eyes to heaven.

That night we pack. We're leaving Italy in the morning. I close my cases, remove them from the bed as Mrs Root comes out of the bathroom. She spots my Italian toiletries tipped into the waste-paper basket, looks in the wardrobe and discovers – abandoned in a pile at the bottom – my new coat, suit, shoes, hat and handbag. She gives a little smile of satisfaction – unaware that I'm watching her. She gets into bed and I climb in beside her.

'Have you packed all your nice new clothes, Henry?' she says.

'No I haven't, as it happens, Mrs Root,' I say.

CHAPTER NINE

'Wilkommen, Bienvenu, Welcome!'

Thursday, 4th July 1991

Driving north from Rome, we pass through Austria, I think, arrive at the German frontier. I feel myself again. I've survived my sternest test, I'm tempered steel, forged in the furnace of Italian volatility. I've had enough sunshine and instability, art and goats, enlarged ideas, hot minxes and tumultuous southern passions to last me for a lifetime. Germany means cool air, manly beer and a willingness to work in the afternoon. I'm driving at an orderly sixty mph.

'That was touch and go, Mrs Root. We'll not do Italy again. We were lucky to escape with our morality intact, our English sense of what's what and who's who.'

'I quite enjoyed it, Henry,' says Mrs Root, who, I notice with displeasure, is reading a picture-book, not on Germany but Italy.

'Nothing wrong with enjoyment in its place,' I say. 'Nothing wrong with leisure activities after work – but your little Italian's at it all the time. They're like children. We'll not find that in Germany, I'm glad to say.'

We reach the frontier, join an orderly queue.

'Must be a week since we saw a decent queue, Mrs Root.' I slow down to allow a Mercedes to pass, admire the driver's hat – a Tyrolean number with a feather in it. 'After you, Fritz. No, I insist. Did you spot his hat, Mrs Root? I might invest in one like that.'

'Self-discipline, Mrs Root, that's the secret. That's the mainspring of your German economic miracle. In 1932 inflation was so bad that a housewife, intent on buying a loaf of bread, was obliged to visit the bakery with a wheelbarrow full of money. By the time she got there, however, the mark had fallen so dramatically that she was obliged to return with a second wheelbarrow. Yet look at them now. Large blonde families with two cars per person and a fridge full of black forest *gâteau*. They like their *gâteau*. We'll get decent food at last.'

'I quite liked the pasta, Henry,' says Mrs Root, who still has her head down in her Italian picture-book.

'Never mind the pasta, Mrs Root. Hard work and sound management, that's the secret. We'll investigate industry, return with tips appertaining to British boardrooms. Did you know that in the time it takes a British Leyland worker to turn out a Mini Metro, your West German worker will have thirty-five Mercedes saloons off the assembly line, taxed, insured, on the road and ready for their first service – not that they need one. Did you know that, Mrs Root?'

'I can't say I did, Henry.'

'We'll visit Daimler-Benz at the first opportunity.'

'That will be enthralling, Henry.'

At last I'd fired the women's interest. 'It certainly will,' I say. 'Mind you – don't run away with the idea that the German is unable to let his hair down. He likes to keep busy, does your German, even in his after hours. Long walks in company, that's his game, throwing things and forming human pyramids. We saw it in Majorca, you'll remember. . . .'

'Ibiza, Henry.'

'There too, I wouldn't wonder. When not throwing things at one another from a distance, eight Germans on a beach will somersault into the water and climb up one another like rats up rigging. Nothing wrong with that. Good clean fun.'

'I'll look forward to that, Henry. I'm glad they can enjoy themselves. I've always heard that they're a little humourless.'

'Based on a misunderstanding, Mrs Root. I read recently that interpreters at the European Parliament have discovered that it takes longer to translate into German than into any other language. Thus, if a non-German speaker attempts a joke, German members will suddenly bark with laughter three minutes after everyone else – by which time the speaker has gone on to discuss child abuse in Romanian hospitals, or some other issue to do with so-called human rights. We'll put this theory to the test.'

We approach the little Bavarian town of Garmisch, arrive at the Post Hotel. As we enter, electronically operated glass doors swoosh open to admit us. I'm impressed.

'German efficiency, Mrs Root. Now we'll test their sense of humour.'

We check in at reception, which is staffed by Helmut, a beaming Bavarian built like a sausage. After the formalities, I decide to test my theory *in re* the German sense of humour. I knuckle the desk.

Back to sanity at last – Germany, to be precise. Helmut, the cheery Bavarian receptionist, greets us on arrival at the little town of Garmisch. 'You know where you are in Germany. You could be in Guildford. It will be a relief not to suffer blowback from the plumbing for once.

'Knock knock,' I say.

Helmut looks bewildered. A poor start.

'Get a grip on yourself, Helmut,' I say. 'You're supposed to say "Who's there?"'

'*Ach – so.*' Helmut seems to have it. 'A riddle, I think. Excellent! Who's there?'

'Hans,' I say.

'Hah! Hans! Very good!'

Oh dear. I'm somewhat discouraged, but I decide to crack on anyway.

'You're supposed to say "Hans who?"'

Helmut brightens up. 'Hans who, eh? I see, I see. This is good. We try again. Knock knock. Who's there? Hans. Hans who? I've got it. Okay – you start.'

I knuckle the desk again. 'Knock knock!'

'Hans who?'

'Hans across the ocean! Oh dear oh dear.'

I rock with laughter, but Helmut remains stony-faced, then turns away, muttering to himself, trying to puzzle out the joke.

'There's truth in the rumour, Mrs Root. No sense of humour after all. Never mind. We'll check out the amenities.'

We move towards the bar, which is separated from the lobby by glass doors. Naturally I expect them to slide open at my approach. Instead I walk straight into them, flattening my face like a cartoon cat's. Helmut and an elderly couple standing by bellow with uncontrollable laughter. They hold their stomachs. They chortle and heave. The barman doubles up with mirth.

'Odd sense of humour, Mrs Root. It's as well I didn't knock myself unconscious. They'd have split their sides. Come – we'll deposit the luggage in our room and then we'll probe and mingle – take tea, perhaps, sample the local *gâteau*.'

Later, we stroll through Garmisch. I'm impressed by the cleanliness, by the feeling of order and affluence. We pass a *Bierkeller*, stop and look at the photographs outside of fat men in shorts, of rollicking blondes, dressed like Alpine cowgirls. We open the door, cautiously peer inside. We are hit by a wall of oompah music and communal thigh-slapping. I hastily close the door.

This agreeable half-timbered tea-shop serves black forest *gâteau* and hot chocolate swimming in clotted cream. Traditional German food is so rich in carbohydrates that until a few years ago, when athletes' diets were scrutinised and strictly controlled, all German performances in track and field were deemed to be wind-assisted and ineligible unless repeated on an empty stomach.

Mrs Root seems to be a little shaken. 'I didn't like the look of that, Henry.'

I hasten to reassure her. 'No reason to be alarmed, Mrs Root. A leisure-intent German will from time to time don short trousers and do a dance, slapping his partner with a sausage. Leather is worn and large quantities of beer are drunk from tankards the size of buckets. We'll look in later – after a nice cup of tea. We'll need to be fortified, do you see? Unfortified, a German having fun bears down somewhat heavily.'

We find a tearoom – enter and take our seats, order hot chocolate and *gâteau*. We are surrounded by smartly dressed, well-behaved old ladies. Mrs Root seems not to have recovered yet from her glimpse inside the *Bierkeller*.

'I didn't like the look of it at all, Henry. All those fat men in shorts. I thought they looked ever so silly.'

'The German by tradition,' I explain, 'has always had a somewhat open attitude as to the body beautiful. Nude dancing in the Greek mode is a favourite pastime, drilling firm young men in army shorts another. It's the dark underside of German culture, Mrs Root. Their need to let off steam sometimes manifests itself in practices as yet unseen in Esher.' I pause, realise that I might be overheard. 'I'll not go into detail, Mrs Root.' I'd forgotten for the moment that English, quite rightly, is most educated Germans' second language. I now notice that the little old ladies are craning in our direction, hanging on to my every word. 'I'll say this much, though. Leather plays a part.'

'Leather, Henry?'

'Precisely, Mrs Root. A German's relationship with leather is absolutely of the essence. It has been calculated that ninety-five per cent of German men wear leather body stockings under their working clothes. Your German's preferred way of letting off steam after personally turning out thirty-five Mercedes saloon cars in a day is as follows: after work he'll shower at home and change his body stocking. Alternatively, he'll lie on a hot slab in a bathhouse and have his backside twigged. We'll look into that later. Then he's ready to put on shorts and do the sausage dance in company. Several buckets of lager later, he'll spew up, exit with his pals and form a priapic pyramid in the street. Nothing wrong with that.'

'It all sounds enormous fun?' says Mrs Root.

'I don't know about that, Mrs Root. Body contact and collectivism, that's his game. He likes to be told. In this respect he's like a child.'

'I thought it was the Italians who were like children, Henry.'

'I'd thank you not to mention Italians, Mrs Root. Your German is a well-behaved child – there's all the difference. If you've had a sufficiency of *gâteau*, we'll return to the hotel.'

Friday, 5th July 1991

We're on the road betimes, drive to Sindelfingen, arrive at the main gate of Daimler-Benz. We're vetted exhaustively on the telephone by an alert security guard.

'That's what I like to see, Mrs Root. Security as tight as a fish's bum. I know fish. I know security. Orlando, the little Mafia hunter, would be as safe as houses here. I'll tip him off. If we were men of respect, we'd stand no chance. My guess is the cleaning lady's armed.'

My credentials having been ascertained, we are driven by a corporately uniformed chauffeur to the Customer Liaison Pick-Up Centre. I'm impressed.

'Nice car. Perhaps they'll lob us one as a souvenir. It's unusual for a touring VIP such as myself to leave the factory empty-handed. Edward Heath, you may remember, left China with a panda in the boot. I'll offer the Jaguar in part-exchange.'

When we arrive at the Pick-Up Centre, Fritz suggests that we join a group which is about to do a tour of the factory in a bus. We board the bus with some twenty other punters, who, Fritz explains, have come from all over the world to pick up their cars and, as part of this important ceremony, are being shown how their new toys were put together.

'This will be boring,' says Mrs Root, who is still carrying her picture-book on Italy.

'On the contrary, Mrs Root,' I say. 'It will be utterly enthralling.'

As the bus snakes its way round the assembly building, Hans, the guide, informs us that between 500 and 700 new cars are delivered daily to customers, further, that ninety-six per cent of the work on these will have been performed by robots.

'That figures, Mrs Root. The Japs send all their robots over here in exchange for German workers, the latter being more efficient. Were we at Honda now, it would be the robots who'd be ducking and diving, reading the *Sun* and taking tea, while the imported Germans did the job.'

Hans then informs us that the robots in this plant produce one car off the assembly line every forty-five seconds.

'Amazing, Mrs Root. In just forty-five seconds that piece of pig-iron there will be a brand new Mercedes, taxed, insured and ready to bomb up the *Bahnfahrt* tuned into the BBC World Service. Someone's onto a good thing, but it's not clear who. On the face of it there's money in Mercedes: you could make a fat living trading in the things.'

'That's what they're doing, Henry.'

'Well I never. You've got a point there, Mrs Root. It's a purring dynamo, driven by Teutonic energy. It's biological. A life-force. No

One of the many *Königsschlösser* perched on the German Alps, *Neuschwanstein* was the home of Mad King Ludwig of Bavaria – one of the most colourful and tragic figures of the nineteenth century. He did nothing for Germany, but he gave Wagner to the world.

wonder they can't switch off. They're driven, Mrs Root – living out their historical purpose. Vindictive spirits and thunderous punishments. Von Rothbart, the Wicked Owl. The dance of the dying duck. The Brothers Grimm. It's the dark, seething under-regions of the German character, you see? The body beautiful and odd philosophy. It's to do with the *Will* and *Wang*. The *Zeitgeist*, is it? The *Doppelgänger*. The *Götterdämmerung*. Thesis and antithesis. Wagner, Nietzsche. Hegel. Heidelberg. All mad. All married their sisters. The tide of history, that was it. *Schadenfreude*. Count Masoch of Baden-Baden. It manifests itself in free-form dancing under an apple tree, prior to being laid out like a fish on a hot slab. See that one over there. Under his overalls it will be a leather thong with a tassel on it. Mark my words.'

The tour completed, we're directed to the Customer Pick-Up Centre, where we're fielded by the tubby head of PR, Detlef Goebel. A serious, well-informed young man, he takes us through to the delivery area, where the punters are united with their new toys.

Every aspect of the car is explained to the new owner, Detlef says, and only when they have grasped the necessary information will they be allowed to drive it away.

I congratulate Detlef on the set-up. 'The place is like an adoption centre. The sharp end of a selective process. They've all been vetted, I

Make mine a Mercedes! Herr Detlef Goebel, the tubby little Head of PR, shows us round the Customer Pick-Up Centre at Daimler-Benz. In the background, the Eagleburgers from Colorado take delivery of their gleaming new saloon.

take it, Detlef? The prospective parents, I mean? Stack up as suitable to bring up a Mercedes, do they? Damn shame to come all this way and fail at the last jump.'

Detlef, who wouldn't win any prizes in a badinage competition, looks somewhat displeased. 'I assure you, Mr Root, that that wouldn't happen,' he says.

I'll not let him off the hook so easily, I feel it's my patriotic duty to be here as Jaguar's representative, as it were.

'Odd system, if you don't mind my saying so, Detlef. The cars are still in the wrong country and so are the Americans and little Japs who own them. No one's any further forward. Except Mercedes, perhaps, who will have already trousered the gooses, I imagine.'

'Gooses, Mr Root?'

'Goose's necks, cheques,' I explain. 'It might have been easier to have shipped the cars to them. Just a suggestion. Don't mind me.'

Detlef insists that the system works excellently, that the punters – together with their families and the family dog – are flown in at a special rate and can now take their new toy for a spin round Europe.

'They'd be well advised to miss Italy,' I say. 'What then?'

'Then they fly back to their own countries,' Detlef says, 'leaving their cars at one of the many pick-up points.'

I emit a sharp, derisive laugh on behalf of Jaguar. 'Without their cars and with an excess of stomach gas. Well, I expect you know what you're doing, Detlef. And I'll say this much. I was impressed by the assembly line. Other EC countries will have something to learn from your economic miracle, your celebrated work ethic and so forth.'

Detlef looks concerned. He frowns. Things are changing, he says. There is no longer the devotion to work that there used to be. The workers are becoming soft, are demanding shorter hours and longer holidays. Each of the workers, in line with new legislation, is now entitled to a paid visit to a health spa for four weeks every three years.

'Do they go?' I ask.

'Of course they go. It is in their contracts. They go.'

'What did I tell you, Mrs Root? We'll visit the baths. Spot a worker being pummelled.'

Detlef then admits that Germany faces many of the problems confronted by our good selves fifteen years ago. Motivation is now a problem. Productivity is still high, but the work ethic is slipping.

Music to my ears. On my return I'll report this discovery to Jaguar.

'A country at the crossroads, Mrs Root. Could go either way, is that right, Detlef? Could be deep snooker, eh? The beginning of the end? Is that the size of it? Well, must be off now, Detlef. Keep your pecker up. Come along, Mrs Root.'

We collect the Jaguar from the car park, head back to our hotel in Garmisch. I'm surprised, frankly, that I wasn't offered a free Mercedes on departure, and I say as much to Mrs Root.

'Never mind, Henry,' she says. 'It wouldn't have been delivered for six years anyway.'

The woman had a point.

Back at our hotel, and delighted with my investigative efforts at Daimler-Benz, I suggest to Mrs Root that we have a drink in the bar. We negotiate the glass doors successfully and I decided to have another crack at testing the German sense of humour. I head towards the lobby, where Helmut, the jolly receptionist, is waiting for me.

'Ah, Mr Root!' he cries. 'There you are at last! Knock knock!'

I'm immensely cheered. 'Who's there?' I say.

'Burt!' shouts Helmut.

I suppress my delight at the coming *mot.* I play the straight man excellently – not my usual role, but there you are.

'Burt who?' I say

'Burt Reynolds!' the fool shouts, with a look of idiotic triumph. He shakes with laughter, pummels the desk, clutches his sides. I move sadly towards the lift, then change my mind. I decide to quiz the fellow about the baths at Baden-Baden, where the workers go to have their backsides twigged.

Helmut, who means well, in fact, lectures me proudly on the health-giving qualities of the baths, the rejuvenating power of a well-aimed jet of water and the effect on the complexion that the bristle-brushing process has. He adds that it his day off tomorrow and suggests that he accompanies us to Baden-Baden, where he'll show us round. I agree, a rendezvous being arranged in the early a.m.

Saturday, 6th July 1991

We drive with Helmut to Baden-Baden, an excellently spick and span conurbation which puts one in mind of Bath – not that I've been to Bath, I'm glad to say. We park the car outside the Roman-Irish tubhouse, where I read some literature appertaining to the twigging process. Helmut has agreed to escort me through it, and I must register some dismay, I think, since Mrs Root now asks me whether I'd like her to accompany me.

'Certainly not, woman. Men's work this. Nothing to it. A few chaps taking a communal tubbing. Nothing wrong with that. Perfectly natural. Naval man myself. Seen it all before. Oh yes. Similar to the after-match tubbing at Twickers. Thirty fellows in a sunken bath. Pass the soap. The up and under. Billy Beaumont. Nothing odd about him. A gentle giant. If it's good enough for him, it's good enough for me. We all know we've got one. Isn't that right, Helmut? Ready for the *douche* are you?'

Helmut now astounds me by saying that he won't be having a bath today, that there must have been some misunderstanding. A heart murmur only allows him to indulge twice a year, and he's had his regulated quota. He has promised to take Mrs Root to see the Schloss Eberstein, he says, some run-down old castle up on a hill, from which Count Wolf von Eberstein is said to have jumped on horseback into the valley below in order to escape his enemies. More likely to escape his weekly tubbing, I think, but I refrain from saying so.

'That sounds enthralling,' I say. 'I'll come too.'

'Don't be silly, Henry,' says Mrs Root. 'You hate that sort of thing. Remember Italy?'

'I'm trying not to, Mrs Root.'

I've drawn the short straw here and no mistake. I'm deposited at the entrance to the baths, where Helmut slaps me on the back. Were it not for his heart condition he'd have got one in the solar plexus.

'You have a good time, Herr Root! We'll pick you up in two hours. You'll come out like a newborn babe! Shall we go, Frau Root?'

I glare at the fool, square my shoulders, tell myself there's nothing to it, that it's all perfectly natural, and duck inside. At reception I use badinage to reassure the lass in charge. Some of her customers will be highly nervous, I imagine, and she'll not want that.

'In one end and out the other brand new. It's the executive car wash for me, my dear. The wax finish, the suction dryer. Hoovering out the interior extra, is it?'

The lass remains silent. I pay and am escorted to the first stage of the process. I'm given a small towel and told to remove my clothes. I do this and am then slotted into the production line, being carried along in the general flow.

I enjoy a joke with fellow customers in the famous baths at Baden-Baden – popularised in England by Edward VII, who came here twice a year to sample the medicinal jets and colonic *douches*. Coincidentally, the bowler hat was invented in Baden-Baden by a German business-man, Hans Bohler. The style was brought to London by Queen Victoria's consort, Prince Albert, and subsequently made fashionable by Sir Arthur Conan Doyle.

As I emerge into the first tiled chamber, a naked attendant instructs me to take a shower, after which I am directed into a warm-air chamber, where, for the first time, I meet the other punters – glistening fat men, laid out like slumbering seals on slatted wooden beds.

A cathedral-like silence prevails – occasioned by general embarrassment, I suppose – so to reassure them I embark on cheerful banter, slap a fat man next to me awake, tell him not to be nervous.

'Nothing to worry about, Fritz,' I say. 'Perfectly natural. We all know we've got one. Billy Beaumont. A gentle giant. Nothing odd about him.'

Fritz remains silent, gives me a wary look. Poor man. He seems very nervous. This will be his first time I expect. I nudge the man on my starboard side, essay a knock-knock joke, recite a verse or two of 'Eskimo Nell' (a favourite in the tubs at Twickers), eventually flop back exhausted by my unreciprocated efforts to relax my fellow punters. By now I'm sizzling like a griddled sausage, am looking forward to cool-down in the next section, am delighted when told that it's time to move on.

I stroll confidently into the cooling chamber, realise too late that I should have accepted the proffered little slippers, that this one is twice as hot as the oven next door. The stone floor is red hot and I dance about like a prawn on a hot plate, cannon into the fat man who'd looked at me warily when I'd slapped him awake. He looks at me with unabashed suspicion now, so I seek to reassure him.

'Nothing to worry about,' I say. 'Naval man. Night ops. Two to the sleeping-bag. Seen it all before. What was it Churchill said? "Rum, sod . . ." Perhaps not. Worse things happen at sea. Pass the soap.'

The next chamber has a shock in store. This is the scrubbing area, where a naked, muscle-bound attendant comes at you with the wire wool and spiked brush. I join a queue of glistening fat men, watch with horror as a punter at the sharp end is flayed alive. When it's my turn to be called forward I offer my place to the man behind.

'I'm in no hurry, Fritz. You'll have a sausage dance to go to.'

Fritz politely declines my offer. I have no choice but to step forward, to relinquish my towel and lie on the slab. The attendant applies the brush – just once, I'll say that for myself. I let out one heartfelt bellow of pain, then catch him a beauty below the heart. He goes down like a sack of meal.

The worst is over now. I find myself in the spa water steam room, perched on a row of tiered stone slabs. We resemble meat on display in a butcher's shop. I regain my aplomb by telling a joke to those in the immediate vicinity. I select my favourite, a forgivably salty one to do with Cardiff. I reach the punch-line – 'No, but my sister has!' – lead the laughter myself, am disappointed to discover that the punters to my right have remained stony-faced. I look to my left, again deliver the punch-line and discover that I am sitting next to three jack-naked women.

'Jumping Jesus!' I cry. 'There are *women* in here!'

Teutonic immodesty in the scouring-room. Either Fritz and I have inadvertently wandered into the ladies' section, or the fat lass on my right has pitched up on a Saturday night instead of a Friday.

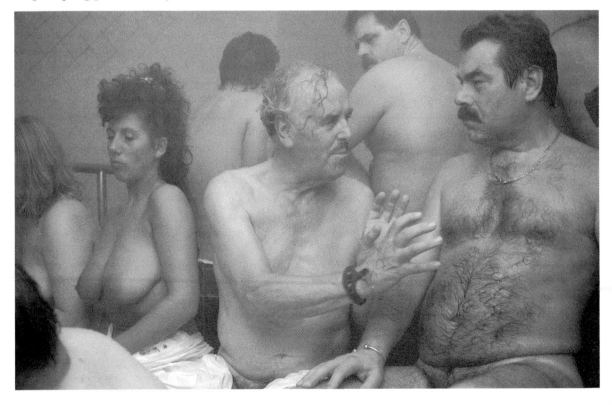

That's it, I've had enough. I attempt to escape but I'm fielded by a posse of attendants who deposit me in a warm, cemetry-quiet, high-domed rest room, in which customers are laid out on tables, cocooned in towels. Only the low, gentle sound of fat men snoring disturbs the tomblike silence. I'm parcelled up myself, laid out on a table with the other slumbering cocoons.

Suddenly one of the cocoons begins to shake with barely repressed laughter. The cocoon next to him asks him why he's laughing. The first cocoon rehearses my joke. I know this because I recognise the punch-line: 'No! But my sister has!'

The second cocoon starts to rock with laughter. There seems a danger he may roll off his table onto the stone floor. Gradually, one by one like a row of dominoes, all the cocoons begin to shake and heave, gripped by helpless laughter.

An hour or so later we're driving back to Garmisch in Helmut's car. I'm in the back, but with my head thrust forward between his and Mrs Root's, as I make them privy to what I've been through. It's not like me to blow my bags but I feel justifiably elated by my achievement.

'A lesser man might have gone under. Not me. Naval man, do you see, Helmut? Oh yes. I've been keelhauled. Slung between the for'ard guns. Towed behind a frigate on a seismic pod. Those were the days.'

I realise suddenly that I have Helmut to thank for this experience. He's not as silly as he looks – and I decide to tell him so.

'I tell you what, Helmut. You were quite right. I feel like a two-year-old. What's next then? Dancing, is it? A bucket of beer, slap a fat man with a sausage and then the priapic pyramid?'

At last I've fired up Helmut, who until now has been a little quiet. He suggests that he takes us to a *Bierkeller*.

'A great idea!' I clap my hands, slap him on the back. 'Watch the road, Helmut. You almost had us there. A *Bierkeller*, Mrs Root! What do you say to that?'

'If you'd like to Henry,' she says.

I sit back happily. 'Good. Good. Let off a bit of steam. This is fun. I *like* Germany!'

Back in Garmisch, we go straight to the *Bierkeller* which Mrs Root and I investigated on the day of our arrival. We are hit by the same invigorating wall of oompah music as we enter, are confronted by rows of swaying Germans. Beer flies in all directions. The band wear shorts. Stubby Bavarian fingers knead the backsides of heavy-bosomed cowgirls. Perfectly natural. All quite innocent.

We sit at a boisterous table. I join hands, sway enthusiastically, slap my thigh.

'Nothing wrong with this, Mrs Root. Harmless fun. A safety valve. Letting off steam, do you see?'

Out of courtesy, Helmut tries to make conversation with Mrs Root. He'll not want to get stuck with her, so for his sake I put a stop to that.

(*Left*) In a Bavarian *Bierkeller*, Mrs Root and I link arms with the carousing locals. It has been estimated that after a normal night's consumption an average customer will be carrying five times his own body weight in excess liquid. (*Below*) I mount the bandstand and, with my *Daily Telegraph* as baton, instruct the assembled throng in a medley of English golden oldies. Later, I teach them the Esher version of the local sausage dance.

I try to jolly him up, tell him a joke, instruct him in drinking songs.

Unwilling to be an extra or mere bit-part player, I decide to lead the festivities. I get up and make my way towards the bandstand. I instruct them in my favourite songs. With a rolled up copy of the *Telegraph* conduct them through 'Knees Up Mother Brown', 'Roll Out the Barrel' and 'My Old Man's a Dustman'. I teach them the words of 'Colonel Bogey', in no time have the whole room singing.

Fritz, who leads the band, now insists that I participate in the German sausage dance. A bladder is produced, I'm lined up opposite a fat man in thigh-tight shorts. He hops to the left, he hops to the right. He does a drum beat on his knees, then slaps me with the bladder round the ear.

I lead the laughter against myself, insist we have another go. I'll not get caught a second time.

The fat man hops to the left, he hops to the right. He does a drum beat on his knees, then slaps me with the bladder round the other ear.

This time I laugh less heartily, call for a time out, then announce that I'll teach them the English version of the dance. I line the fat man up, hop to my left and catch him with my *Telegraph*, send him flying off the podium, head first into a pile of tankards.

Honour is satisfied. For the moment I've had enough. I return to our table, where Helmut seems to be on the point of leaving. He asks Mrs Root whether she'd like him to escort her back to the hotel.

'A kindly meant offer, I'm sure,' I say. 'Thank you, Helmut, but I fancy Mrs Root would rather stay and enjoy herself. Isn't that right, Mrs Root?'

'Of course I would, Henry,' she says.

That's all right, then. Thus satisfied that Mrs Root is having a good time, I return to the podium and instruct the room in a medley of Dame Lynn favourites – 'The White Cliffs of Dover', 'We'll Meet Again' and 'Maybe it's because I'm a Londoner'. I must have got Mrs Root back to the hotel somehow, I suppose, but I can't remember how.

Monday, 8th July 1991

Two days have elapsed while we drive to Flensberg, north of Hamburg, where I intend to quiz one Beate Uhse, who, I'm informed, dispenses items of erotica under plain cover.

When we reach the industrial estate from which she trades, I stop and car and instruct Mrs Root to produce the camera.

'Follow me,' I say. 'I have in mind an *aide-mémoire* for Hussey, but we'll not want the world and his wife to know our business.'

I find a deserted spot, line myself up in frame.

'Right. Audio-visual *aide-mémoire*. "The Root Report on Europe".'

Entry Six. Flensberg. Having beaten the Germans at the sausage dance, I've arranged a rendezvous with Beate Uhse – a Luftwaffe fighter pilot, who participated with distinction in World War Two but now purveys novelty lingerie through the post. Already the most successful exponent of sexual liberation in Germany, so-called Miss Uhse might, unless checked, corner the Euro-market in once-a-week apparel. That's my fear. If there's to be immodesty in Esher High Street it best be supplied by Branson. Hence my visit. Cut!'

Back in the car I tell Mrs Root to hand me the map supplied by one of her staff.

'Won't be easy to find,' I say. 'It will be an undercover operation – probably a box number or hole in the wall. She'll come in once a week to pick up the mail, thereafter dispatching the stuff from her back room.'

We drive round a corner and come face to face with an enormous modern factory with Beate's name blazoned on its roof.

'As I expected, Mrs Root. Typical of the Germans to shout about it.'

We park the car and enter the reception area. The atmosphere is bright, friendly and efficient. The staff on duty are smartly turned out, pretty young lasses. I'm reassured. There's nothing sleazy here. I knuckle the desk, inform the lass on duty that Beate's expecting me. After a minute or two an elderly, respectable biddy appears and escorts us to an impressive boardroom, where Beate is waiting for us. She is a tanned, wiry little woman in her seventies, of the sort one sees participating with distinction in the veterans' section of the London Marathon or disporting herself with credit on the tennis courts of Budleigh Salterton. She grips me with a gnarled claw, says how glad she is to meet me.

'The privilege is mine, madam,' I say. 'You had a good war, they tell me. Well done. Bombs away. Firm but fair. Honourable opponents. No hard feelings. We've forgotten Dresden even if you haven't.'

I've put her at her ease. She suggests we sit round the boardroom table, where we are joined by Irmgard, the elderly assistant. Had I harboured any fears that we had entered a disorderly house, Irmgard's homely presence would have reassured me.

'Nice old tart,' I say to Mrs Root. 'She wouldn't involve herself in anything below the belt.'

'So, Mr Root, what can I do for you?' Beate says.

I tell her that I'm currently researching Europe for the BBC, looking into lifestyles, indigenous practices and *mores*.

'You're in nightdresses, I believe,' I say.

'Well yes – among other things,' Beate says. 'We also produce books, magazines, videos, sex aids of one sort or another. Perhaps you'd like to see our latest catalogue. Irmgard!'

Irmgard fetches the catalogue and hands it to me. I open it

carefully, squint at it from a distance. One doesn't in the general run of things care to view this kind of material with ladies present.

'Nothing wrong with this,' I say. 'Saturday night apparel. Upstairs once a week after supper. Not my cup of tea, of course, but there you are.'

Beate asks me whether I recognise any of the young lasses modelling the outfits. She uses mainly British girls, she says, because they have the best figures for this type of work. My patriotism is stirred by this piece of info. I feel quite proud.

'Is that so, Beate? British bosoms – excuse me, Mrs Root – are best, is that the size of it? A thought occurs. I'm with Branson, do you see? Some of his leisure products might slot well with this stuff here. I'll have a word with him on my return.'

Beate asks me if I'd like to see some of her other products. I agree enthusiastically. There could be stuff here for me and Branson. Novelty items. Comic ashtrays. Carnations that squirt water. Revolving bow-ties. Canine whoopsies. Irmgard leaves the room, returns shortly with a pile of items which she places in front of me.

'How interesting,' I say. 'Branson will . . . Jumping Jesus! What have we here?'

I have in front of me a range of frankly obscene material – electronic phalluses, explicit books, pornographic videos, Japanese love balls,

With ladies present notwithstanding, Frau Uhse – Germany's leading exponent of Saturday-night apparel through the post – hands round samples of her product with the coffee and *petits fours*. Mrs Root won't have seen these before. I find myself on the horns of a dilemma. Would this stuff mesh with Branson's?

battery driven condoms in all the colours of the rainbow. I take up a handful of brightly coloured condoms.

'Attired in these,' I say, 'three men could link arms and go to a fancy-dress ball as the Italian flag. This stuff's disgusting, madam.'

'Come come, Mr Root!' Beate says. 'Simple aids to greater pleasure! No one is compelled to buy our products. They know what they're going to find when they enter one of my shops.'

'I'm glad to hear it, madam,' I say. 'This is not the kind of stuff one would wish to be confronted by when queueing for one's suppositories at Boots.'

This brings on a burst of the usual liberal guff. Repression and censorship cause more problems than they solve. Ignorance is the enemy. What consenting adults do in the privacy of their bedrooms and so forth. I've heard it all before – not least in Italy from the little Cicciolina minx – and I agree, without enthusiasm, when Beate offers to show us round her packing room. We leave the boardroom, walk to the area where the mail is sorted. Envelopes are being deftly opened, large mounds of money form. Crisp girls wheel trolleys up and down long corridors, piling them high with products. Beate informs me that she has just acquired two million new customers in East Germany, further informs me that she is looking for franchising partners in the United Kingdom. She suggests that I take some samples with me back to London. I eye the ever-spiralling mountains of currency, do calculations in my head.

'Nothing wrong with this sort of stuff,' I say. 'Perfectly harmless. An aid to – excuse me, Mrs Root – sexual pleasure. Keep it out of the wrong hands, of course.'

'In the new Europe, Mr Root,' Beate says, 'it won't be the large who'll eat the small, but the quick who'll swallow the slow.'

I square my shoulders. 'We'll not be swallowed, Mrs Root. We'll not want that.'

I thank Beate for a most enlightening hour or so, allow her to pile me high with further products and then depart, assuring her that after a word with Branson I'll be in touch.

Once outside, back in the cool morning air, certain moral qualms return. As we drive off, I apologise to Mrs Root.

'Sorry about that, Mrs Root. Hadn't realised that the dark underside would be laid out with the coffee and the biscuits. Insensitive of them with ladies present. Blame myself in a way. Shouldn't have involved you.'

'That's all right, Henry,' says Mrs Root. 'Naval wife and so forth.'

What does she mean by that? There have been slight, subtle changes in the woman since we left home almost a month ago – remarked on hitherto. Small alterations in demeanour, in modes of speech and attitude, which might not have been spotted by someone less alert. Had I not known better I'd have suspected some sort of leg-pull here, an ironic undercurrent. I'll not have that, I'll not have ironic undercurrents in the marriage. I decide, however, to let the matter pass.

'Watch out for a quiet spot,' I say. 'We'll ditch the more explicit stuff behind a hedge. The brazenness of it, Mrs Root! Laid out with the coffee and the *pot-pourri*.'

'I don't know, Henry,' she says. 'They seemed like respectable people. Mind you – I can't imagine who'd buy all that stuff. Putting the cart before the horse, if you ask me. Like owning all the right golf clubs but having no idea how to play the game.'

I can't follow the analogy, I must admit. 'I don't know, Mrs Root,' I say. 'I've got all the right clubs.'

'So you have, Henry,' she says. 'So you have.'

There she goes again – the unaccustomed inflection in her tone, an odd expression on her face. I'll puzzle it out. I'll not have ironic undercurrents.

Further down the road I stop at a stretch of countryside, decide this will make a suitable dumping ground. I get out of the car, load myself with disposable erotica, struggle with it to a field and force myself backwards through a bramble hedge. I turn round – laden with motor-driven phalluses, filthy books, bondage bars, leather thongs and flailing rubber dolls – and find myself eye to eye with a fresh-faced family of hikers who have stopped for sandwiches.

I spin through 360 degrees and dive backwards through the hedge, dropping a phallus or two as I exit. I hurry back to the car and open the boot. Just then two little old ladies drive up in a Volkswagen.

Never mind the environmentalists. I decide to ditch Frau Uhse's inflatable filth in open country. Branson can make his own arrangements.

'Is this the way to Schleswig?' one of them asks.

'Mind your own fucking business!' I shout.

Uncharacteristic of me – a sudden lapse – but I have been sorely tried. The little old ladies drive off with squealing tyres and I hurl my load of filth into the boot of the car.

'Just our luck to find the busiest place on the road,' I say to Mrs Root. 'We'll dump the stuff tonight. In Amsterdam. Coals to Newcastle. Dreadful place. Our final challenge. The last leg of an historic expedition.'

'I've heard Amsterdam's ever so nice,' says Mrs Root. 'I'm looking forward to it.'

'And that's a mistake, Mrs Root,' I say. 'Amsterdam poses a triple threat: drugs, sex and pollution. The indigenous population is as high as kites on substances and the place is sinking at the rate of six feet per annum. Largely the fault of our good selves, I'm glad to say. Thanks to toxic emissions from the UK, the sea level is rising steadily, with the satisfactory result that Amsterdam will have disappeared entirely by the year 2050. And not before time in my opinion.'

CHAPTER TEN

'Le Pays Bas: Nul Point!'

We arrive in Amsterdam in the early evening and quickly become entangled in a maze of canals and narrow side-streets. I drive in circles – narrowly escaping collision with spaced-out younger elements on bicycles – always arriving back at the same point.

'The man who designed this city must have been on drugs, Mrs Root. A psychedelic nightmare. Drugs, sex, debauchery at every corner.'

By a stroke of good fortune we suddenly arrive outside the Krasnapolski Hotel, where I have booked rooms for one night. That should be enough for Holland. I instruct a porter to unload the Jaguar completely.

'We'll leave nothing in the open overnight. Lucky if we've still got a car in the morning, I imagine.'

I say much the same to the lass in reception when she hands me my key.

'Here you are, sir,' she says. 'Room 274. I hope you enjoy your stay.'

A recent picture of a Dutch windmill.

'I very much doubt that, madam,' I say. 'A sink of iniquity at first sight. Drugs, young women in windows, *laissez-faire* at street corners.

A woman's work is never done. Driving through one of Amsterdam's residential quarters, we observe a house-proud young wife busy with her Monday night chores.

I'll be saying as much when I call on your Chief of Police tomorrow. What the hell are you staring at?'

I turn round, notice that the porter has unloaded my pile of pornography from the boot of the Jaguar and has placed it ostentatiously on top of our luggage. A bondage bar falls to the floor, is recovered by a passing matron. A rubber doll shows signs of self-inflation.

'It's for His Grace, Duke Hussey,' I explain. 'I work for the BBC, you understand.'

Tuesday, 9th July 1991

Up early for my meeting with Commander Bob Visser, the head of Amsterdam's CID. I check my watch, discover we have an hour or so to play with, decide to take a short stroll round the city.

This is a mistake. We attempt to cross a main road, are driven back by clattering trams, bell-ringing cyclists and honking motorists. At one point a break in the tramline allows us to reach a temporary oasis a third of the way across the road, where we are perilously marooned by hurtling traffic in the other two lanes.

'This is madness, Mrs Root. On drugs the lot of them.'

Eventually, by dodging courageously in and out of traffic, we arrive on the opposite pavement. Passing a café, I decide we need refreshment.

'I could do with a brandy, frankly,' I say. 'Better keep off the hard stuff, though. Don't want to give the wrong impression at Police HQ. Let's see what they've got.'

I inspect the menu, remark to Mrs Root that they seem to have an outstanding selection of coffees on offer.

'Moroccan, Afghan, Colombian, Jamaican, Lebanese, Home-grown Grass. What's that got to do with it? A local health fad no doubt. What do you fancy, Mrs Root?'

'Just a *cappuccino*, I think, Henry.'

I order from the chap behind the bar, observe that the chocolate cake looks good.

'Two *cappuccinos* and a brownie,' he says.

'A brownie, Mrs Root?' I say.

'Not at the moment, thank you, Henry.'

'Um, this is good,' I say, taking a bite. 'I'll be having another brownie, I think.'

The stop off had been a good idea of mine. Half an hour and three chocolate brownies later I emerge from the cafe feeling as right as ninepence, more cheerful, in fact – euphoric almost – than I remember feeling since we left Esher almost a month ago. Mrs Root, however, still seems disconcerted by the traffic.

'Oh dear, Henry,' she says. 'We'll have to cross all those roads again.'

'Nothing to it, Mrs Root!' I cry. 'Follow me!'

I negotiate several main roads, floating confidently through cyclists, cars and trams – all of which are forced to take sudden evasive action.

Some of Amsterdam's young people are customarily so drugged that they fall off their bicycles and into a canal.

'I'm on top of it now, Mrs Root,' I report triumphantly. 'The trick is to take the initiative, to press on regardless. Ha ha! Look at him!'

There is a satisfactory splosh as a keen cyclist goes head first into a canal.

We arrive in no time at Police HQ, where we are directed to Commander Bob Visser's office on the first floor. Bob, with whom I feel an immediate rapport, I don't know why, greets us warmly.

'So, Mr Root,' he says. 'You are researching Europe for British television? How can I help you?'

For some reason the answer to this question quite eludes me. I struggle to harness my wandering thoughts, am prompted eventually by Mrs Root.

'Henry?'

'Yes?'

'The Commander wonders how he can help you?'

'Is that right?' I say. 'How very good of him.'

This response strikes me as amusing, I don't know why, and I start to chuckle to myself. Then I notice a crack in the ceiling above our heads, wonder how long it will be before we're buried under a pile of plaster.

It's odd this: I'm finding it hard – almost impossible, indeed – to concentrate. That's not like me. As I've said before, my powers of concentration are, in the normal run of things, quite exceptional. A lesser man, suddenly experiencing novel sensations – a not disagreeable light-headedness, a disordering of the mental processes, a certain alienation from the immediate environment, coupled with the opposite feeling that one is perceiving everyday objects for the first time – certainly from a new angle – an acute awareness of self and a sense of being locked into the present (that time is standing still) – might panic.

Not me. I have the answer in a flash. I'm suffering from Jaguar lag, from the syndrome vulgarly known as '*autopiste* madness'. I've simply been overdoing it, covering too many miles in a day. I'm fortunate. My symptoms are mild and not unpleasant. I've heard of people suddenly bursting into tears and lying on their backs in the road with their legs in the air.

The diagnosis arrived at, I feel even more cheerful – euphoric almost, as after an operation, I'm told, when one floats peacefully between a dream world and reality. I force myself to grapple with the matter in hand.

'I'll tell you how you can help me, Bob,' I say. 'Drugs. I gather you encourage them here.'

Bob overreacts. He's as transparent as a pane of glass. I can see straight into his brain – an odd sensation, I can tell you.

'*Encourage* them, Mr Root?' he says, with overstated emphasis. '*Encourage* them? That's very far from what we do. It's our view, simply, that drug abuse is a social problem – not properly a matter for the police. We regard addicts as victims, not as criminals.'

That's what I think he says, at least. The fact is he no longer has my full attention. I've become distracted by the ordinary – but suddenly strange – objects on Bob's desk (a table lighter, a memo pad, which I start to read, a photograph of Mrs Visser and three delightful children), equally by some mementoes of my visit to Beate Uhse's factory – a gaudy suspender-belt, a phallus pen, a packet of obscene playing cards – which I produce from my pocket inadvertently when delving for a cigar.

What's this doing here? At a telling moment in my interview with Commander Bob Visser – the *Guardian*-reading head of the Dutch CID – I inadvertently fish a suspender-belt from my top pocket. I explain to Visser that it's one of Branson's.

Bob is speaking.

'Mr Root? Is everything all right?'

I don't at all like his tone of voice, find his sudden interest in my welfare quite uncalled for. What does he take me for?

'I'm perfectly all right, thank you very much,' I say. 'Why shouldn't I be? What are you trying to suggest?'

Bob backs off quickly. 'Nothing at all,' he says. 'Nothing at all. So – your misconception about the Dutch attitude to drugs. We see ourselves as part of the educative process. Drug users have many problems, of which addiction is only one. For instance, if I now went into the street and saw an addict on the pavement giving himself a fix . . .'

'You'd feel his collar, right? You'd bang him up in the – er – in the . . .'

The Jaguar lag has taken over. I can't imagine where he'd bang him up. The Hilton, is it? A hospital?

'I wouldn't bang him up at all,' says Bob. 'I wouldn't arrest him. I'd encourage him to join the methadone programme, on which his habit could be controlled.'

I chuckle at this young man's naïvety. Controlled indeed! Not cured – merely taken off one dependency and put on another. I'm about to make this point, realise instantly that I can't be bothered. Bob is banging on.

'Furthermore,' he says, 'so that young smokers of cannabis, say, are kept out of contact with dealers in heroin and cocaine, the authorities have separated hard and soft drugs. Certain licensed cafés are allowed to sell cannabis either to smoke or in the form of cakes.'

'I don't like the sound of that,' I say. 'What if . . . what if . . .'

What if what? The point I wish to make utterly eludes me. I muster my scattered thoughts, decide to get on top of things.

'The point is this, Bob,' I say, 'your liberal, "who cares?" policies are putting at risk precisely the most vulnerable members of society.'

That's got him, unless I'm much mistaken. A bull's-eye. A hole in one.

Bob's one of those who doesn't know the meaning of defeat. I'll say that for him. I smile encouragingly. I'm enjoying this joust with my young opponent.

'Our policies, Mr Root,' he says, 'may be liberal but they are anything but uncaring. To whom, anyway, are you referring? Who are these vulnerable members of society?'

'Airheads, Bob. The unemployable, single-parent liberals, street derelicts, the weak-willed. One sniff of cannabis and the brain drops out. Shrinks to the size of a plum. The skull caves in and eventually you swallow your head.' I'm motoring now, I'm on a roll. 'Everyone knows that. It's statistically proven that before you know where you are it's pass the heroin, *por favor*. Isn't that right, Mrs Root?'

'I certainly hope not, Henry,' she says.

The symptoms of my Jaguar lag are becoming less acute. I'm slightly distracted still, but find it easier to follow the conversation.

'I'm a little concerned by what you're saying, Mr Root,' continues Bob. 'We're far from being complacent, and our policies do seem to be working. In spite of the easy availability of cannabis, the number of users has declined.'

He's fallen into my trap.

'Of course it's declined,' I say. 'They're all on heroin and cocaine!'

Bob still won't concede.

'Once again, I'm happy to say that you're entirely wrong, Mr Root,' he says.

'Thank you very much, Bob. Glad to have been of help.'

'In fact,' he says, 'the percentage of young heroin users is decreasing fast. The latest figures show that only four per cent of Dutch addicts are under the age of twenty-one. Seven years ago the figure was fourteen per cent. Do you realise what this means?'

Time's winged chariot . . . I check my watch, decide I could do with another 'brownie' at one of Amsterdam's many agreeable little cake shops.

'Of course I do, Bob.' Damn me – the Jaguar lag's coming back. I search for the meaning, but it's as elusive as an orange pip. 'Er – what?'

'It means,' says Bob, 'that young people are not experimenting with heroin in the way they used to. Our policies are working. Statistics conclusively refute the theory that cannabis users will move on automatically to hard drugs.'

I'm unimpressed. In the knowledge that I have a world-class argument up my sleeve, I let forth a derisive – though not unkind – hoot of laughter.

'Ha!' I ejaculate. 'Statistics! You can prove anything with statistics, Bob.'

I've made my point. I've won hands down. It has been a clean fight but a fair one. I've had enough.

'I'll be off now. Come along, Mrs Root.'

I get to my feet, pause at the door to deliver a Parthian shot.

'Do not judge others, Bob, by responsible elements such as my good self.'

Satisfied that I've upheld decency against the liberal Dutch, I return downstairs with Mrs Root and leave the building.

'Quite an agreeable young man, Mrs Root,' I say. 'But what a lot of nonsense he talked! Did it strike you he might have a drink problem?'

'I don't think it was such nonsense, Henry,' she says. 'Their liberal policies are obviously working. Their record with drugs is clearly the best in Europe.'

'I dare say it is, Mrs Root,' I riposte, 'but who'd want to live in Amsterdam, anyway? An irrefutable argument, I think you'll agree.'

Having bested Mrs Root – in itself nothing to write home about – I suggest that we stop off at the little café we visited earlier.

'Frankly,' I say, 'I could do with some refreshment. You'll not have spotted anything amiss, but during my meeting with Bob, I was suddenly subsumed by Jaguar lag. Now I feel as right as ninepence. I have the chocolate cake to thank for this, I think. What do you say?'

CHAPTER ELEVEN

Home Sweet Home

Thursday, 11th July 1991

The epic adventure is nearly over. My theories have been corroborated everywhere; I've prevailed in every confrontation; I've corrected the little foreigners as to their thinking; I've upheld the English way of doing things; I've faxed Hussey with my findings. This journal speaks for itself.

I've covered everything, I think, save for a telling incident on our return to the United Kingdom – indicative of something, though I don't know what. At Dover Harbour I hand our passports over to the young SAS man on undercover duty, whereupon he says:

'Had a good holiday, did we, sir?'

'*Holiday*, John!' I say. 'Would you have said that to Sir Francis Drake after Trafalgar, to Henri Coeur de Lion on his return from Agincourt?'

'I don't think I was on duty that day,' he says. 'On your way, Admiral.'

Home sweet home. At Dover Harbour, I banter with a cheery undercover SAS officer. Thanks to Lady Finchley, so-called Jacques Delors' 'no-frontiers' policies will cut little ice on this side of the *Manche*.

'A prophet is not without honour, Mrs Root,' I say, as we pass through immigration. 'Sticks and stones. Broad shoulders and so forth.'

I slip 'We'll Meet Again' into the Jaguar's tape facility, sing along with Dame Lynn as we drive through Kent.

'You're very quiet, Mrs Root,' I say. 'You all right? Weee'll meet agaaa-in, don't know . . .'

Rule Britannia! Even the trees stand to attention in this pastoral Esher landscape.

'I'm fine, Henry,' she says, 'really,' but she continues to stare out of the window rather dejectedly, unless I'm much mistaken.

'Good, good. That's the ticket. Home in a couple of hours. Don't know where, don't know wheeee-n.'

I survey the green fields of Kent, my heart swells with patriotic pride.

'The Garden of England, Mrs Root. Your traditional oast-house, your old hop-picker, your indigenous sheep, your local cow. There's something four-square about your British ruminant, is there not? Weeee-ll meet agaaain . . .'

As we drive through Esher's leafy avenues, approach our own familiar street, park in front of our own front door, I sum up for Mrs Root.

'A moment to savour, Mrs Root. The weary warriors return. Tired but triumphant. Battle scarred but unbowed. A nice cup of tea would go down well. Any brownies, by the way?'

Later in the lounge-room, while I bustle through the accumulated mail, Mrs Root unpacks the collected memorabilia of our journey – picture-books, little packets of soap, some Spanish lace, the model of a matador, another of a tarantella-dancer, an Italian vase, a concertina of Black Forest picture postcards – and places them in a cupboard. She still looks a little sad, I think, so I attempt to jolly her up.

'Good to be home, Mrs Root,' I say. 'I'm glad that's over.' I go to the window, gaze proudly across my acre and a half. An appropriate snatch of poetry comes to mind. '"England with all thy faults, I love thee still – my country! I'd not exchange thy sullen skies and fields without a flower for warmer France with all her vines."'

The swell of the verse fails to enthuse the woman. She closes the door on her small, sad souvenirs, sighs wistfully and starts to wipe the accumulated dust from shelves and tables.

'It's the small things, Mrs Root,' I say, as I pace my lounge-room. 'The rich man in his castle, the poor man at his gate. Decency and order. Common sense. An absence of talking in the open air, of windy abstractions and barren theories. My *Daily Telegraph*, your *Daily Mail*. Old Lord Deedes. The Lee-Potter woman. Gold Top milk. The British bobby on his beat. Nothing surprising, nothing untoward. Stop and search. Hygiene and repression. Knowing that Monday follows Sunday. Early closing. Bolloms the cleaners. "They'll be ready on Thursday." The licensing laws. "Time Gentlemen, please!" Big Ben and *News at Ten*. *That's Life*. *Ask Anneka*. The little conjuror. Esther Rantzen . . . oh my good God!'

I've cast myself down. My shoulders sag, my spirits droop. I don't know why.

'A sherry wine, Mrs Root?'

'Not while I'm dusting, thank you, Henry.'

I go over to the globe cocktail cabinet. I'm about to open the

Northern hemisphere, when my eye is caught by a substantial land mass to the west.

'Ever thought of going to America, Mrs Root?' I say.

I go to my upright portable, pause for a moment's thought, pummel the keys.

President Bush   The Anchorage
The White House   Lakeside Avenue
Washington   Esher
                                               Surrey

                                               11th July 1991

Mr President,

You'll not know me. I intend shortly . . .

The Statue of Liberty
beckons us to the
Land of the Free.
This will cost a
bomb. 'Dear Hussey,
I have in mind . . .'